A
Harlequin
Romance

McCABE'S KINGDOM

OTHER
Harlequin Romances
by MARGARET WAY

McCABE'S KINGDOM

by

MARGARET WAY

HARLEQUIN BOOKS   TORONTO
WINNIPEG

Original hard cover edition published in 1974
by Mills & Boon Limited.

© Margaret Way 1974

SBN 373-01863-0

Harlequin edition published March 1975

Printed in Canada

1863

CHAPTER ONE

SUCCESS. She wanted it, now she had it, or what passed for it. Happiness. A Career. She had one, not both. The odd happy minute came as a wonderful surprise. There was plenty of excitement in the theatre, plenty of feeling, but no inner peace, just a restless striving after that elusive thing, perfection, or at least a kind of professional excellence. Even in the sphere where she had won critical acclaim, she had no sense of belonging. She had never belonged anywhere, not for many long years past, and she was continually aware of it, though her *identity* had never been in doubt.

She was Shawn Grenville's daughter, a man who had lived out his short life like a torrent, oscillating between the joint achievements of writer and actor. Had he lived, he might have become a figure of some mark in the theatre, but she had lost him when she was barely twelve. Lost his rapid force and direction, the agile wit and original mind, left for ever with a deep spring of sadness for the great might-have-been.

An orphan, or near enough, at twelve. Child into woman. The onset of the stormy and terrible teens. For her, anyway. Her mother, Carole, was quite different — alight, with a selfless good humour. A wonderfully endearing sort of woman, quizzical, a little vague, radiating that ultimate gift, contentment. Wise about many things, she often admitted to being a born failure when it came to understanding her firstborn, her daughter Katia, though they shared a love so eloquent it dismissed all other considerations; the curious, unbreakable silver links of the mother-daughter relationship, whether workable or not. Quite simply, as Katia came to see later, they wanted and needed different things. What one sought and enjoyed, held little interest for the other.

Katia's temperament, for good or for bad, was her father's. Moody, mercurial, yearning, artistic. No charming conceit, but a fact so complete, Katia often thought her mother found it a penance, for she had never understood her husband, either. But she was forever grateful for Katia's most tangible inheritance, her physical beauty, which was considerable and had set her apart from that moment in hospital when the doctor declared he had delivered a rose.

It was the swift, darting intelligence, the sharp, incomprehensible yearnings, which were the mingled source of pride and great trouble, for Katia's mother had an innate distrust of academic brilliance in girls. She saw it, quite clearly, as more of a hindrance than a help – in the light of her own experience, a reasonable enough assumption. Shawn had always claimed he loathed clever women, so that often it seemed to Katia that to be mildly stupid with perhaps her own face would have been a great blessing. An excess of anything bred resentment – in friends, their mothers, so that once she had actually tried to fail her examinations in deference to the hopeful sea of faces at prizegivings.

Of course, she hadn't. Try as she might, Katia Grenville was different – a lonely thing to be. Grudgingly accepted, now at last vindicated as someone worth while, a bright new star of the theatre, at twenty-three, moving in a sphere where her gifts were accepted as naturally as air. But she wasn't happy. She almost expected never to be. Even her beauty wore a brittle air. Her face in the mirror had a fine, clear outline, with a look all her own. Blue-lustred black hair swung in a heavy arc from a partingless widow's peak. It contrasted sharply with a gardenia-pale skin, densely fronded blue eyes.

'Jewel flowers,' Thorn had called them, the first time he had seen her, and they had been full of tears then. Thorn and his quick, easy comfort, milk and honey to a displaced and hypersensitive child. *Thorn*. Her eyes fell on the twin photographs that never left her dressing table whatever theatre she played in. Thorn and her father. The world would come to an end before she forgot either of them. Two men so different, each exerting a powerful influence. Stranger yet again, Thorn was closer to her in many ways than her own mother. She never baffled Thorn. Family, yet not family. No relation at all, only her mother had married Thorn's father, to be widowed again, ten rewarding years later. A one-step meteoric rise from a struggling young widow with a small child, to the enviable position of the firmly entrenched landed élite, sure of their position in society. The wife of Charles McCabe of Carunya, a cattle kingdom that rose out of the empty, endless plains, flinging its gargantuan arms across South-West Queensland and almost into the Territory.

The McCabes were among the pioneering giants, gentlemen squatters who had forsaken the fringe of Colonial civilization for the lure of the purple ranges and the lonely, unexploited plains. The McCabes had their own history, beaten out under the drumming army of the cattle they marched across the arid wastes. Their privations had been frightful, but the rewards had proved great. Cattle and horses had made their fortunes over and over again. The old agonies and the deaths in the desert had only strengthened their determination to hang on. The rude huts had given way to mansions in the wilds. Man defying his primitive environment.

Katia sat very still within her bubble of quiet, suspended for a moment in time. She was back on Carunya, a familiar experience. Even now it haunted her dreams. Thorn was there. Thorn was everywhere, even here, where he had no place to be. Thorn *was* Carunyah now. A man so sure of himself, *born* so sure of himself and his destiny, he never had to question himself for a minute. She twisted her head and her eyes fell on the photograph.

'Don't look so guilty, Kat! Don't ever be afraid to look at me!'

She could almost hear him saying it, for Thorn missed nothing with his slanting black eyes, brilliant and disconcertingly perceptive. Thorn was a man, tough, arrogant, formidable. The very cast of the face and mouth foretold it. Yet he had a strong streak of humanity, a dark, dangerous charm, that dash of tenderness he used so softly and skilfully – especially on her. She had been Thorn's small pet by adoption. He had taken over the role of 'big brother'. Unfailingly patient, when he was not patient by nature – taking her side in all family discussions, then propelling her firmly into the world she claimed she craved for, doing everything in his considerable power to aid and abet her, so that even she couldn't remember all the details.

If she was a success, she owed much of it to Thorn. She had revealed all her ambitions to him, tumbling them out, and he had listened, paying attention as only Thorn would, working in his own way towards making them come true. Her heart gave a quick lurch, a mixture of feelings that went deep and she couldn't fully understand. A path through quick sands. Sometimes she resented the time she wasted on Thorn, for she was perpetually in the grip of her memories. He would only laugh at her in any case. Her vagaries of mood and temperament cut no ice with Thorn. Her blue eyes or her accomplishments, her calms and caprices came equally to him, the treatment different, but the manner the same.

Thorn. He was already a man when she had been a child. Twenty-four to her twelve. Half a lifetime again. She could never catch up to him, for all her crusading zeal. He had struck at her childish vision with unquenchable life, his days crammed with colour and violence, orders and decisions, yet creating for her, right from the beginning, the illusion of belonging, taking her over as his own small follower. The *odd* one. A conqueror surveying a new-found, captured possession, sardonically accepted and all with such steely strength. If his undertaking was to make life easier for her, then he had done it.

In the mirror before her, his dark face lay superimposed over her own. Thorn knew every trick in the trade at keeping her bound to him. She was under no illusions. Thorn had a motive for everything, a black velvet voice in the scented darkness. She loved Thorn as if he were her own, yet sometimes she grew weary of the very thought of him, like a much-loved tormentor at her side. Perhaps she was as he claimed, 'colossally inconsistent', but her name was still Grenville. Her two little stepsisters were McCabes, but she had won her small victory there, for they had wanted to make her one of them. The McCabe brand on everything. No lingering reminders of that other life without them.

At some curious level she was fighting a duel with the McCabes, and that meant Thorn, for he was head of the family now, though he was the only one who had ever been kind to her. Thorn and his reasons; as numerous as the sands of the sea. She *had* to have this life of her own, to keep her identity, her pride all intact. Then, perhaps, he would let her go. She wasn't one of them. He had fulfilled his duty, shown her how to escape her giant, faceless background, her mother's well-meant and earnest machinations to marry her off, see her 'safely' settled; a manifestation of the depths of her own worries concerning her daughter and her lack of faith in Katia's own ability to look after herself.

Well, she had done that and well for the past four years, even if she had to accept Thorn's monthly cheques in the early days. The cheques still kept coming, paid into her bank, but she hadn't touched one of them. Her own name now had a certain lustre. She had achieved a dream, but where was fulfilment? There was a party to go on to, some small escape, refuge and fantasy, but she didn't want to go. For once she craved quiet and blessed obscurity. It was cold in the dressing room and she shivered in her thin silk robe. It was time to get dressed. The performance was over, a good deal of heavy work, for it was tautly constructed and rather startling in places. An experimental production. *Eccentric*, one critic had called it, and she was inclined to agree with him, but she had her own small, faithful following and she drove herself to a set standard. If only her followers knew of the nerve storms behind the polish and poise! She had, and she could play comedy, but drama held her main triumphs, for she had, if the critics were to be believed, a quality that 'drove at the heart'. Beauty and bravura, Ivor liked to call it. Rashly Ivor also wanted to marry her. Long practised in the theatre as one of the very best producers, he now had an entirely new reputation as a playwright of astonishing candour.

The Group, her current success, was Ivor's own play and production and it was acid and stylish like Ivor, if not entirely original, but it was good of its kind and well received by the press and public alike. Katia wondered what her mother would have made of it. She hardly knew what to make of it herself. In fact, at one point in the first act she was always seized by the faintest impulse to laugh. She would have told Ivor, but Ivor would never dream of laughing at himself. Tiredness was pressing on her intolerably.

A knock came at the door. It opened and she swung around looking directly at Ivor d'Arcy's super elegant good looks, the tall, spare figure that carried so well his fashionable clothes.

'Darling, that was clumsy of me! You're not ready yet?' She made a little grimace and shook her head. Clumsy was the one thing Ivor undoubtedly was not. She bent to pick up a long scarf she had worn in the last act and he bent to forestall her.

'I love you!' He said it as if it was the most pressing thing on his mind. She stared back at him with her bluer than blue eyes as if he had said no more than 'It's raining!' He had to reach her somehow. He leaned forward and caught her slight shoulders, desperate to make contact. She had the most disconcerting knack of going away from him, a will-o'-the-wisp quality that compelled him to force her attention. 'Tired, my lovely, elusive Kate?'

'A spinning head!' she said with an attempt at an apology, her voice falling smooth as silk on his ears. She knew how he felt, yet she rose swiftly to her feet with a lightness and grace that pleased and annoyed him, for he wanted only that she should fall into his arms, not spring like a startled doe away from him.

He waited for a moment until the sensation of her nearness and his own response subsided, then he tossed off in a brisk, businesslike tone:

'Quite a good house, really. The front rows were a bit thin!'

'The rest of the house was full, so why complain?' Katia said quickly. Beautiful, intense, flippant, she walked behind the tall screen that stood to the right of the dressing table in front of a long built-in wardrobe.

'Oh, I'm not, darling!' Ivor said dryly. 'Whether people understand or not what I'm getting at, they do come. For various reasons, if only to decorate the stalls. Best of all, a far sprinkling of the hard core professionals turned up. You were superb as Marcia. A black rose. Such a relief after Elsa who's never entirely audible. A pity, because she has *some* potential. Remind me to chat her up about it, would you?'

'I will!' Katia promised, her voice muffled as she pulled over her head a long slither of black crêpe, lit with a pattern of silver and gold thread. Her hands were shaking slightly, as they always did after a performance, but she ignored it, as she reached inside the wardrobe for her black satin evening shoes. Ivor was still talking in his deep, slow voice, but she scarcely heard him as she waited to unwind. It was always like this for her, a very personal thing, and mostly Ivor understood, never intruding, but she had the unhappy notion he was going to ask her to marry him again. She surprised in herself a sinking feeling, as though she was being called upon to shoulder a burden. She shook out her hair and came from behind the screen, the light falling over her still, serious face.

'She came in like starlight, hid with jewels!' Ivor quoted with a sudden recourse to sources not his own. 'Let me say simply, I like it. New?'

'Umm!' she murmured, endearingly offhand, seductive and fragile at once. She might just as well have been ice-bound. With an unaccustomed flare of action he spun her into his arms, where she remained, fascinated by the unexpected.

'Do you care for me at all? Or do you care about anyone?' She wasn't meant to answer, for his hand came under her chin lifting her head, the pressure of his mouth causing her to struggle for breath.

'Please, Ivor!'

'Why shouldn't I kiss you? You look the most beautiful and desirable of women, yet. . . .' His lips moved on her own, painful and abrasive, and his hand caressed the line of her back. 'A thing of grace! Marry me, Katia. I'm the only one who'll ever understand you, you're such a temperamental little creature!'

She pulled her face away as if he had struck her, so

that he halted, his own face burning, his hazel, green-flecked eyes showing the intensity of his feelings. 'Do you do it deliberately?' he asked tautly. 'The Circe call, then the violent reaction? What's with you, Katia? Do you like to experiment?'

Her mouth was throbbing, a physical mark he had left upon her, her hair massy in its swing, as glossy as a blackbird's wing. She spread her hands silently, eloquently, goading him to a sudden insolence.

'Don't act with me, pet. I've heard about the others!'

'Then you've heard nothing!' she said with perfect truth. 'No dark morass of intrigue.'

'Oh, hell, I know *that*!' Ivor shrugged elaborately, implying heaven knows what, 'but there's something. Someone, some nameless element.' He broke off abruptly and looked at his watch. 'Let's end this fruitless discussion. Come along, darling, there's really no reason to quarrel. I said it at the beginning. I was clumsy. You're tired, that's all, and now a party in the middle of the night!'

She came back to the light touch with difficulty. 'Be honest, Ivor, you love them!' she said, her head tilted away, a little heart-chilling coldness over her breast bone. It was Maggie who had worked *temperamental* to death. The implacable Miss Maggie McCabe, who even now treated her mother as a guest on Carunyah.

Ivor didn't know this, but his perceptions, extraordinarily acute, decided on a quick glance he had mortally offended her, his words hitting and hurting like blows. He said no more, knowing in many ways she was as secretive as the Sphinx, but devoted himself to

14

effectively getting her out of the theatre, across the car-park into his car, as if some weighty enterprise depended on his success.

Dexterously he swung the Jaguar out of the narrow, confined space and into the main channels of traffic going over the Bridge. The party was at Point Piper, at the particularly hideous old mansion of Lady Rushmore, a society hostess of some consequence. As many of the usual ultra-sophisticated mob as could comfortably be fitted under the one roof. Still, she was a pleasant enough old battleaxe, Lady R., Ivor reflected, and better still, forthcoming with a little necessary financial backing, which was more than he could say for a lot more attractive ladies. He began to whistle tunelessly under his breath and eased the Jaguar into the right lane, outbluffing of all things an Alfa Romeo. The needle, which had suddenly picked up, dropped back again and he turned to glance briefly at his companion.

The pale, perfect profile presented to him was as chaste as the moon goddess, absorbed in its own thoughts, melancholy, mysterious, and he had the greatest urge to interrupt them, give her a good shaking up. Loving her as he did, he could still be intensely irritated by her — her cool inviolability, the walls of reserve that reared tower-high. Sometimes he felt the only good straightforward thing he could say about her was that she had no conceit whatever in her beauty or ability, not knowing either that Maggie McCabe had regarded both as a frivolity to the point of sin. He felt faint with all sorts of excessive frustrations and his mind began to wander.

He was hungry, for one thing. He hadn't eaten since

seven that morning. It was as well he was driving to a medieval plunder. Lady Rushmore was justly renowned for her gargantuan post-theatre buffets. Too much food. Too much drink. Too much of everything for the asking. Too many people professing to adore the theatre to have fallen under the spell of his latest venture, professing to find it profoundly satisfying, anxious to seize on its subject matter and worry it to death like a bone. Worst, too many men crowded around Katia, silent for the most part, their inane chatter halted, because that was the effect she had on them, so dark and neat-boned with her pale oval face rising like a flower on a single stem. Katia, how he loved her, right from the beginning, though he didn't know it then.

'How's your mother?' he asked suddenly, prosaically, in an effort to gain some response at all. He had met Carole McCabe once and found her charming, in an entirely different and more comfortable way than her daughter.

Katia started a little, and turned her face to him. A space traveller, back. 'Oh, I'm sorry, Ivor! I'm not very good company, am I? I feel a little fey tonight, as if something is about to happen. Mother is well enough. She still misses Charles unbearably, but she won't come and live with me, though I ask her and ask her. Charles wanted her on Carunyah and there she will stay. She's still mystified by my choice of a career, in any case.'

'I can't think why, my love!' Ivor said dryly, lifting his eyebrows. 'One or two people still remember your father. The people that count, you know. It's not as if you're involved in any real disaster. Damn, it's raining

16

again!' He leant forward and switched on the wipers.

'It doesn't make it any different or any better,' Katia supplied. 'The theatre to Mother is a floating, insubstantial world where ends never meet. It was for her with Father. I know I shall always baffle her, but I do love her and she loves me. We have that to be grateful for. Always at the back of her mind I think she has some faint hope that I'll suddenly tire of it all and go back to Carunyah.'

'*Back*, not home?' Ivor asked quietly. 'You talk like an orphan. Yes, exactly an orphan. In any case, you know quite well you can't go back there. See, you've got me saying it. For the theatre to lose you now would be a crying shame, let alone me! I can't face the thought of it. Curious, because I'm not a marrying man!'

'Who is?' she asked gently, and smiled.

He slanted a smile back at her. 'Shimmering light eyes! Quite beautiful, Katia. But seriously, I can't imagine anything more dreary than the Outback!'

'You haven't seen Carunyah, which might shake a few of your fancies. In any case, you're bone lazy, Ivor darling, the life wouldn't suit you at all. To rise with a mother-of-pearl dawn. Scalding billy tea round the camp fire!'

'I see!' he said agreeably. 'It's not exactly tactful of you to point it out, you heedless young thing. Sometimes you make me feel as ancient as those sandstone hills of yours. Now tell me, what about that Machiavellian relative of yours?'

She swung her head towards him with seeming astonishment. 'Who in the world do you mean?'

'McCabe!' Ivor said bluntly, knowing her rather better than she thought. 'The Lucifer type, black brows drawn, you have on your dressing table.'

'Ivor darling, you do have a passion for drama,' she murmured at length, some suppressed emotion vaguely surfacing. 'Thorn is a striking-looking man, if that's who you mean?'

'Who else?' Ivor said with some satire. 'I hate to mention it, my lamb, but just occasionally you dissemble rather badly. From the look of your Thorn, he's the type that doesn't give a purple damn for anyone or anything, yet he seems to care about you.'

'He's been kind to me, yes. As a child who hankered after kindness, I got more than my fair share from Thorn.'

'You're uncommonly easy to be kind to!' Ivor said in a slightly tart voice. 'I'll guarantee he's perfectly indifferent to a lot of other people – especially the ones without black hair, a white skin and blue eyes!'

'You sound like a man with an ardent desire to make a scene,' Katia cried, following his hardened expression with her eyes. 'You're not, are you, darling, because I'm so terribly tired. I can't really think what's wrong with me. I've never felt quite like this before. In fact if you shout at me, I shall weep.'

'I reserve my applause!' he said with some humour and a lingering trace of asperity. 'You did that beautifully, I haven't the brutality to continue. I suppose I should rid myself of a burden and tell you I'm as jealous as all hell of your king with a paper crown, McCabe. In fact now we touch on him I can't hold my tongue, and your reaction makes me more decided than ever. You're not in love with him, by any

18

chance?'

'I dote on him, does that satisfy you?' Katia asked lightly.

'My mind is perfectly made up,' Ivor retorted with unaccustomed persistence. 'May I suggest that if you really want to change it you begin by acting quite differently towards me in the future. If I lose you, I lose everything. This McCabe excites a little too much of your admiration. Even your voice changes when you talk about him, though my heart aches the way you try to hide it. Thorn McCabe, a curious phenomenon in your young life. Is it possible you kneel down and worship him?'

'I've too much respect for my knees,' she said, looking at him with faint anxiety, her eyes shadowed. 'Please, Ivor, you're acting abominably all of a sudden – this one-sided conversation veering towards the tragic. I never realized you felt so strongly about Thorn when in actual fact you would like him.'

'I wouldn't, I'd hate him!' Ivor said with perfect truth, but his face lightened and he reached out one hand to caress her cheek, tenderness behind the gesture. 'And I have to find a weapon against him!'

Katia gave a little exclamation of distress and touched her fingers to her head. 'If you only knew how my head was aching you'd stop all this nonsense!'

He bent towards her, his voice full of concern. 'My poor child, why didn't you tell me? I'm so sorry, and I've been tormenting you. Is it very bad?'

'Sheer agony!' She looked back at him, but her mouth twitched.

'I ask myself, should we go on? I'm becoming so utterly unselfish, a sure sign of care. I thought I had a good life, Katia, yet it's nothing now without you. I feel giddy at the prospect of having you all to myself.' He glanced at her face again. 'I mustn't be talking very clearly. Can't you hear what I say? Marry me, Katia. You'll never regret it.'

'How can I know that?' she smiled, and lightly touched his arm.

'Dreadful girl! You dare not love someone else.'

'Well, not very seriously, anyway!'

'Capricious female! One day you'll be desperate to accept. You might consider that at least half a dozen of the women who will be here tonight, not to speak of the old girl herself, are madly in love with me!'

'Lucky for them! You're such a charming fellow, Ivor, and I *do* love you. A little.'

'A golden reward! Don't say another word. You're quite impossible. A little? How hideous! I'm not sure if this isn't one of the worst moments of my life. Warm, silky and fathomless with mysteries, that's you, Katia my love, but McCabe will never get you, not if I have a small say in it!'

She said quite conversationally, her eyes on the rain-swept road, 'You sound quite violent, Ivor. It's not like you!'

'Then you've made a mistake, my girl. Not your first. Passion *is* violent. Vulgar if you like and some-times downright ridiculous. I'm only artistic in my plays. The way I sound now is infinitely more reliable, believe me.'

'You melodramatic idiot!' she said with taut affection.

'Next to impossible to shake off. I'm wonderfully tenacious when it comes to getting something I want,

Katia darling.'

'Well, your tenaciousness is exhausting me right at the moment. I've just found myself, Ivor. I thought you of all people understood that. For some little while I want to be in full possession of my soul.'

'Oh, but you're not, are you?' he asked dryly, his face a frieze in the dim light from the dash. 'It's taken a little courage to speak out tonight. All this apparent nonchalance, the stolid and the unemotional, is just a pose. I didn't want to frighten you off, but I happen to need a few signs of your awakening. This McCabe has an hypnotic influence on you and I'm not insensible to it as you thought. After all, it may be true that he was kind to you as a child, but damn it all, you're a child no longer and so maddeningly cold. A miracle of beauty, yet you're driving me demented. What I want I can't have.'

Her slight figure seemed to droop like a cat on to a cushion. 'Do you really think this conversation is doing either of us any good?' she asked tiredly, in her voice a tinge of strain. 'I feel chill to my very bones!'

'I'm sorry, darling,' he answered very gravely, 'the heavens might fall, but I can't stop myself now. Put it down to a few neat whiskies on the quiet. I want your love. I want you so badly, yet I have this damnable idea that something, *someone*, is separating us. Besides, confession is good for the soul, so they tell me.'

'They should have told you it doesn't fall quite so easily on the ear of the listener.'

He laughed a little, low in his throat. 'I'm afraid you're right. A hundred pardons, my love, but you don't seem to realize how very easily you hurt me, how very unhappy you alone can make me. But let it be a warning to you, you're not the only woman in the world, even if you're the only one I happen to want!'

'Therein lies the answer!' she suggested too innocently. 'The fascination of the apparently unattainable. That would appeal to you, Ivor.'

His eyes slid over the ivory gleam of her face and shoulders. 'I can't fault your psychology. The more urgent I become, the more you retreat from me – *me*, with all my stifled emotions, and you do cut to the heart. Always remember, Katia, and I'm a lot older than you are, it takes a little courage to be what you are. All the mistakes and defects, the brutal little bits. You've opened my eyes to a flaw in myself. I'm a jealous man and jealousy is ugly, belittling, with a hint of real danger, and all the while I keep smiling and talking while you become an obsession with me. Take McCabe now, and I'm forced into bringing him into the conversation, for no concrete reason. I see him as a shadow that lurks at your side. I have a feeling he'd go with you wherever you went, not just his photograph, though God knows that's irksome enough. Up until now, he's been a name unspoken between us, yet without him in the background the stage could be set for perfection.'

She hesitated only for a moment, her voice very grave. 'You think so?' Her breath fluttered, perhaps with her own intense and unexplored feelings.

Ivor tossed her a tight smile, his face oddly held. 'Don't storm me with a question. I *know* so, my lamb, and don't lose your temper. The trouble with you, Katia, is you don't know me very well and you don't even try. You use me, in a way. We're constantly together. I take you everywhere. People say, there goes poor old d'Arcy, laid low at last. You see no one else, I've checked that thoroughly, though I'm a fool to admit it. You don't really feel for me at all. The star on your forehead has got into your eyes!'

'Oh, Ivor!' She made a small sound of agitation and fell silent, not even trying to find a comment. Ivor in this unquiet mood was a revelation touching on depths she hadn't even known he possessed, though she should have, for he was too good a writer.

'Sometimes it's necessary to hear a few home truths!' he said.

'They hurt. What do you want me to do, Ivor? Do you have the right to question me, really?' Her voice started to tremble despite her control.

He felt her body stiffen and he touched her hand, long slender fingers. 'It's quite simple, darling – do this and I'll trouble you no more. Be more considerate towards me, kinder. You're a careless little cat with my heart in your hands.'

'Never that!' she said, stung.

'I didn't say intentionally. In a lot of ways you're as soft as a dove, and better still, you're the only woman I know who's as interesting to talk to as a man!'

'Yo, ho, ho!' The quick return to his usual style made her laugh. 'That's more like you, Ivor. I'm very flattered and proud. Thank you so much, you're such a dear, kind, *conceited* man!'

The relief in her voice made his own voice grow dry. 'That's all right, darling, most men in my place would have said it. Your face alone has its own awesome draw!'

As usual, any allusion to her beauty seemed to grate on her. 'Whatever pretension to beauty I have, I consider unimportant!' she said with magnificent scorn.

He laughed, fully expecting her answer. 'How foolish you are, Katia, and how very young, after all. Beauty is *never* unimportant. Often, it alters one's destiny. A fine pair of eyes alone can reap undeserved rewards. Earthly rank. Earthly riches. Non-stop intrigue if you have a mind to it. No, don't interrupt. Your keen intelligence should suggest to you that looks *are* important. You surely don't think that bloody fool Richards relies on his brain power. Stupidity is no great drawback when you look like him.'

'Really! I find him quite dreadful, despite all the shine on him. In fact, he puts me in a brooding, sombre trance. Frank, now, is so much more interesting.' She seized on another member of the cast. One she knew Ivor particularly disliked for whatever reason.

'That wizened leprechaun!'

'He makes me laugh!'

'That beard and those prominent eyes!'

'For all which, his love life is legendary!' she pointed out with delicate sarcasm, surprising in herself the unfamiliar urge to sting him as he had stung her.

'Maybe so, but in all conscience I can't agree with you. Frank Barclay in my opinion, which should count for something with you, is one of the caprices of nature.'

'And a very fine actor!' Katia continued, not even knowing why she was doing it. It was all so meaningless, but she knew the desire to hide behind any form of subterfuge. 'Frank is an expert at the macabre. *The Group* would have been lessened without him.'

'Agreed, but let's forget about poor old Frank. We'll see enough of him tonight. Even at my brightest and best, discussing the various excellences of other men is not my forte.'

She moved a little closer to him and smiled. 'I'm experiencing some pretty distressing symptoms myself. Please don't let's stay long tonight.'

'Whatever you say, my love.'

The wicked inappropriateness of it later amused Katia, for they stayed on almost to the bitter end with every appearance of pleasure, until finally, taking the initiative from Ivor, she got up in one liquid, languid movement that still managed to convey, in silence, her imminent departure. Ivor, on cue, broke off his one-sided conversation, looking over his shoulder to catch the gleam of her polished skin, the massy swing of her superbly cut hair. Suddenly he felt marvellous, a glow inside him. Katia *and* the intoxication of achievement! It must be showing, he felt so drunk with it.

With an easy, sidelong gesture, he touched his lips to Lady Rushmore's paper-dry cheek, suffered gracefully her massive hug, staggering for an old lady, and made his way towards Katia, watching her cast her own charisma, waving and smiling her farewells. A clamour rose within him, an agony of wanting that made the whole thing irrevocable.

Outside the night had a metallic silver sheen. Rain-washed roofs and pavements. No one anywhere. The streets seemed deserted.

'Well?' said Ivor, in the heated comfort of the car. 'Wonderful, wasn't it?'

'Wonderful!'

'For a voice that can convey almost every sentiment,

25

that wasn't worthy of you, darling. Don't go mono-syllabic on me. And all my favourite food. You must admit the old girl can really turn it on. She knows good food!'

'*And* drink!' Katia volunteered with a sidelong look at him. 'I never see champagne without thinking tenderly of her.'

She heard Ivor's amused laughter. 'Frank made an irretrievable fool of himself!' he said without smiling and in some satisfaction. 'I'm not greatly surprised. The only thing that does surprise me is that he's never been given in charge.'

'Then we have that to look forward to!' she murmured, trying to relax a bit.

'Do I detect a faint sarcasm in that line?' Ivor inquired, drawling a bit.

'You do!'

'Well, never mind! The thing is, my darling, I'm not sure if this new thing of mine isn't the most exciting bit of theatre I've ever done. It will take you to communicate my heroine, of course. You're such a marvellous technician, and I write for technicians. Ashton was kind enough to say, "Now sits expectation in the air!" Even so, you could transform the most intractable part.' With a small frown of puzzlement he flickered a glance at the perfectly quiet and uncritical Katia. 'You might show a little interest, darling!'

'I'm terribly tired, Ivor.'

'Standard reply!' he said dryly. 'You mean you don't want me to come up?'

'That's the briefing!' she said lightly, and smiled. 'But I *do* love you.'

'I just hope you mean it, and not for the sake of

26

conversational politeness. If I'd only taken more time wheedling a little more sherry into your glass. Ah well, just settle your head back and we'll do the rest of the trip in silence. I won't sleep myself. The creative bubbles in my head. All the old girl's champagne! A clever bloke, Ashton. Underpraised for such a master of invention. He's given me quite a good line to go on. Sorry, darling, I caught the faint sigh. I won't talk now when there's really no need. I'll bring the script around tomorrow. A long, lazy Sunday and dinner at that new place, Toselli's. They tell me it's a revelation and no ghastly loud music to contend with!' He could see her skin gleaming in the pearly, soft darkness and he steeled himself to accept something; she was a small silent oasis in all the bright talk. 'For someone who was just recently the life of the party, I'm wondering about you, Katia my love.'

With her dark head lying back against the upholstery she suddenly smiled at him, and his resentment faded, melted away along with all the crowding questions and the problems he might have to face. There was nothing to be gained by rushing her, the realization was overwhelming, but one thing helped him enormously – she shared no sense of identity with the McCabes, whatever else she felt, and it was a kind of insurance against possible defeat. Perhaps it was, as she claimed, a sense of loyalty and gratitude that made her capitulate to that Outback dictator. He knew the type, with an arrogance that was practically ineradicable. Still, he was no small puzzle, Thorn McCabe, and eventual confrontation lay at the back of Ivor's mind. It was as well he had received rigorous training in the art of acting civilized, for he had the ridiculous notion

27

that when it came to Katia, he was not. She had only to
smile at him and he was lost. A mark of the glorious
irrationality of love or violent infatuation or whatever,
for he had a first-class attack of it, and late at thirty-
eight.

Katia was impossible to capture and pin down. So
much so he was afraid of the elusive 'something' in her,
and always the worry that he might lose her. She was
Woman, with all the secrets in the world to fathom out,
spoiling him for anyone else, a fact that equally ap-
palled and fascinated him. It made no difference at all
to her that he was considered by some to be a tremendous catch. She was not gratified in the least, unlike the
other women he had squired about. Katia was rare, to
the extent that her most commonplace gesture had
become a benediction to him. In short, he 'had it bad',
as the saying went.

On a passionate wave of reaction he considered in-
sisting on going up with her, then decided against it.
With Katia there was always a welcome, but not what
he wanted. She was so self-contained she might just as
well have grown up in an orphanage, presenting to the
world only what she wished them to see. She was quite
inexplicable and he had an enormous compulsion to
see her against the giant background in which she had
never found a frame. *Carunya*. Every intuition warned
him; only there would he find the key.

CHAPTER TWO

It was Ivor who had found her her sixth-floor apartment in the elegant town house designed by his friend, Stewart Deighton. It was ideally situated, yet perfectly private, inside its walled banks and cloistered terraces, with fine views of the Middle Harbour the dazzling effects of the city's lights by night, and the pure enchantment of sunlight and waterscapes in the morning. She was very happy there, with her images of the sky and the ocean, lavish with her love and her money, trying to make a home for herself.

She must have succeeded to a degree, for most of their friends had at first credited the decor to Stewart's hand, a designer in total, as gifted as he was crushingly expensive. But she had worked her own magic, using her own judgment plus a few beautiful pieces contributed by some of the theatre people at her housewarming. Blue was her colour. She loved it. All the different tones from the dreamy to the brilliant. Mixed with white; mixed with green, touches of gold. Blue was for romantics. Was she that? She thought so, but in that respect, she had the certain feeling Ivor found her wanting, calling into question whether she had, in fact, anything to give anyone. Was it as Ivor said: there's always one who kisses and one who turns the cheek. More likely, the averted cheek was turned, in vain, towards a third, unseen person.

The lift made its swift, silent glide to the sixth floor and she stepped out into the corridor, carpeted a deep topaz. Pictures hung at intervals along the walls, adding to its hospitable look, yet she surprised a curious tension in herself, a variety of sensations she was at a loss to find a cause for. She slipped her key into the door, only to find it unlocked, the small entrance hall abloom with lights, repeated in the floor-to-ceiling mirrored panels. Her mind grasped at his presence before her eyes ever saw him, lending her face such light, like a soft explosion of stars, that the impact of her beauty was doubled.

'Thorn!'

She moved forward in her long dress, floating into his arms, the reason for his presence for the moment entirely irrelevant. She turned up her face with a child's spontaneity, all the music and emotion in the world in her expression. His black eyes kindled as he bent his dark head.

'Kat! Always more beautiful than I remembered!' His lips brushed her cheek with a brief contact. 'Can't I ever startle you?'

'No!' She laughed a little, feeling all the old pleasure and excitement, sustained and gladdened by his presence, the deep, cutting edge of his voice. She tilted her head back, to look at him, the dark and forceful uniqueness of him. 'I've had this feeling all evening something was about to happen,' she said happily. 'I can't explain it. Intuition, I guess, or E.S.P., though I haven't been practising it. Thorn?' She broke off uncertainly, chilled by omen as much as the odd restraint in him. The finger of fate touched her and she shivered, the colour dying out of her face with frightening suddenness. 'Thorn, what is it? What's happened?'

He stood above her, a steadying authority in his stillness alone, his black slanting eyes unfathomable, yet she could name what she felt . . . apprehension. It leapt for her, making her aware now that his presence was both sad and frightening. What lesser power could have brought him so many miles from Carunya here, at that hour? A sense of inescapable disaster settled on her; her mind crowded with details that all resolved themselves into one comprehensible picture.

'Mother!' she said with a funny little gasp, a queer desperate sound that longed for him to contradict her, her mouth and her wide, aquamarine eyes the only colour about her. But the set of his head was answer enough and her sense of balance went without warning and she clutched at him. *Thorn.* The only real strength she had ever known.

'It *is* Mother, isn't it?' she said, no longer needing an answer. 'And I like a fool so excited to see you. Not another thought in my head.'

His grip on her shoulders was harsher than he intended; her reaction affected him more closely than he cared to admit. The light had died thoroughly out of her face and he felt momentarily helpless, a position he would never relish. Sick panic had struck her so that she held herself tightly under his hands. Her eyes filled with tears, the jewel flowers he remembered, almost a shock to the senses with their size and purity of colour. A waiting stillness was in her body, turning her at once into the Katia of old, the one small girl the whole family had quarrelled over. She looked desperately frightened, like a tortured child, so that over-reacting, he shook her hard, not liking the over-brilliance of her blue eyes.

'Stop it, Kat!' he said with forced detachment.

'Surely you've learnt by now, if you go through life expecting the worst, you usually get it. It *is* your mother, but she's going to be all right, I promise you. She's suffered a stroke, but she's come through much better than we dared hope.'

'*A stroke?*' She said it as though it were un-identifiable, the first tremors hitting her. In her face was a dreadful foreboding that he found hard to watch, adding to his own concealed anxieties, and he held her shoulders, forcing her head up, not allowing her to surrender. She didn't look grown up at all, in fact she looked just like the night a good ten years back when Starlight's foal died after they had sat up all night longing for the little chestnut to frisk its delicate legs and begin sucking ferociously. Of course it hadn't, and a superb colt had been lost. Even now he was left standing between her and the extreme sensitivity he knew so well. She had always been a handful with her gaiety and sadness, the swift sudden changes from tears to delight, and she had always called forth his com-passion.

'Kat!' he said with a half impatient tenderness.

A flicker of something near hostility flashed in her eyes. All the old resentments, the buried emotions of her years on Carunya. Things she wanted to forget. Carunya. It still towered over her life, over all their lives, even Thorn's. Big enough and wealthy enough to have a life all its own. Not the man owning the land, but the land dominating all the human figures with its extraordinary drawing power. Maggie and her bitter, incomprehensible dislike, all the more potent for being three parts submerged like an iceberg.

A pathetic longing not to blame Thorn for anything

showed in her eyes and he gathered her closer, sweeping her off her feet and carrying her into the living-room. She seemed much too light, and she aroused the same deep feeling in him that he had for all small wild creatures. He sank into an armchair, feeling the shocking tension in her, her head back against his shoulder, the graceful, proud neck, the silky hair, thick and raven against her sharp pallor.

'Katia,' he said slowly and rather hypnotically, 'I can't compel you to listen, but you will, won't you? That's my girl!' His hand slid under the silk of her hair. 'I told you your mother is going to be all right. If it's humanly possible, I'll make certain of it.'

There was a kind of frantic denial of this in the way she swung her cheek against his hand. 'Certain? Why are you so certain? Even the great Thorn McCabe can't be certain of anything. A stroke! I can't believe it, much less accept it. When did it happen?'

'Mid-morning yesterday.'

There was the shock of his voice again, hard and bracing, and her elegant body became rigid, her voice soft and severe.

'And you never told me?'

'I came myself!' he corrected her, subduing her with his damnable authority. 'As soon as I was able. You see, I know you too well, Katia – how you react. No cables, no long-distance phone calls. I came myself, and I'd like you to consider for a moment what it was like for the rest of us. I was way out on the Run, the first time in over a month. Rance, the young fool, took up the chopper the quicker to spot me and only succeeded in nearly wrecking it and himself. One of the other boys rode for me. Maggie for once lost all good sense. The children were helpless with fright, literally speechless by the time I got back. Every last house girl gone to the pack, wailing in a way not easy to shake off, let alone stop. It was utter pandemonium until Armstrong arrived!'

Katia's bare shoulders in the lamplight were as touching as a child's, not seductive at all, and they suddenly relaxed. Because of his firmness and his tautened face her shaking stopped.

'But a *stroke*, Thorn? I can't bear it. I can't associate it with my lovely mother. She's so young, so active, and she takes such good care of herself!'

'She's forty-seven years of age,' he said quietly, and the shadow of his hand fell across her face. 'It's happened, Katia, and we must go on from there. Mercifully she's been unaffected beyond a slight paralysis along the left side of her body. We're hoping that will respond to therapy. Armstrong's been very good. He's fixed us up with a trained nurse, a good woman, cheerful and competent, and your mother likes her, but there's no one like Katia. I've come to take you home – for some little while anyway. Would you come at the cost of risking your career? This d'Arcy you wrote so much about?'

'Tell me when you're ready to leave,' she said, not missing the old, tantalizing mockery. 'What *is* my career anyway, compared to my mother?'

'I agree, because I share your strong loyalties, but your career has made you what you are – a success. It was what you wanted, remember?'

Her eyes lay with vacant attention on the fine cloth of his jacket. 'I know, but I can't say I'm happy!'

'You expect too much, little one,' he said lazily. 'You

always did, but one day you'll arrive at the only solution for you. Your sure place in the world. No reasoning required, just instinct.'

There was an odd, unexpected note in his voice and she turned her head, her eyes touching on his beautiful mouth. 'Oh, Thorn!' she said quietly, 'the sweet tyranny of the past. You always seem to be there, telling me!'

'Cheer up, darling!' he said lightly, the lamp gilding his bold incisive profile. 'We're all rather proud of your success, if you're not. Especially your mother, even if she's wondrously uneasy about life on the stage.'

'The *wicked* stage, you mean,' she said, and laughed for the first time.

'You said it, jewel-flower!' The smile was reflected in his hard, handsome face. 'Still, it's nice to make a triumph out of a minor disaster. People who succeed in life are usually different. *You're* different. You always have been, but the really piquant thing about you is, you tend to apologize for it. Success goes with your attitudes, the energies you've got. Most people can't make an effort, or sustain it at any rate. Success is, as you've found, like anything else, one has to work hard at it. *I* have to. Even with an inheritance like Carunya I can't just sit on it. The land is an endless vision. I'm not just holding it for the next generation, my son – I'm building, improving on it, advancing my father's dream. We all carry the torch for something. Besides, little one, I suspect you have the odd moment when you feel marvellous because you are who you are. Katia Grenville, a gifted young actress, your father's daughter, the torch-bearer. It shows, anyway, darling. Each time I see you, you're more beautiful, more polished, a finished product, with everything going for you. Until you start to cry, that is, then you're silly, sweet Katia. The original *enfant terrible*! Feel better?' he asked, a mocking indulgence inflecting his voice.

'Yes!' she said as freshly as a child. 'You're so wise, Thorn, and I dearly love you, Big Brother!'

'Do you now? That's nice!' His black eyes sparkled sardonically, and she made a small half-hearted swipe at him.

'Mocking devil! You know, you're a very arrogant man, Thorn. Not *horrible* arrogant, but bred in the bone. No wonder at all you haven't troubled to marry. I ask you, who would be worthy?'

Heavy lids hooded his slanting eyes, gently rebuking. 'How do you know, impertinent brat, I don't intend to alter just that in the very near future?'

'After the horse sales, I feel sure!' she flashed back as dry as ash. The horse sales were famous on Carunya and Thorn's great passion. Thorn and his horses with their matchless, aristocratic beauty. Affectionately she turned to smile into his eyes, raising her delicate black brows, and for an instant something quite different and uncontrollable flared through her, a hard knot of excitement that threatened to overcome her, induced by the nonchalant superiority of his head, the dark copper sheen of his skin, the brilliance of his black eyes.

Swiftly Katia averted her own head, lest he recognize her strange lack of restraint, her small face intense, tendrils of some fearful emotion clutching at her throat, while all the while he lay back in the armchair as lazy as a big cat, studying her in silence, his eyes ranging over her seemingly frozen elegance, then all in one disciplined movement he set her on her feet, standing over her, one hand on her shoulder.

'Might I recommend, Katia, my changeling, you start making a few phone calls, or rather, the all-important one. I know it's late, but I'm sure he won't mind. I want to leave at first light, but I'll grab a few hours' sleep first.'

'Here?' she tendered rather dazedly, almost swaying under his hand. 'You could use the sofa. It's very comfortable.'

'It sounds it!' he said, black eyes glinting in his amused, male face. 'But alas, baby lamb, just that bit unconventional. I'm a stickler for them.'

'The devil you are!' she said softly, shocked.

'I am. *Now*,' he corrected, then moved to the door without haste. 'Don't hold your breath any longer, Kat. Release it or you'll suffocate. Now, go and ring Ivor, and mind you waste no words. I'll be back!'

Katia stood for a few seconds in the empty room as though rooted to the ground. Thorn was inflammatory stuff at the best of times, cynical but so helpful, and there was no one else like him. But the things you enjoyed were not always good for you. Still, she reflected wryly, it was worth it to stand near the fine blaze that was Thorn's. Knowing what he expected of her, she moved then, as swiftly as she knew how, and crossed to the telephone.

Ivor, as he mentioned, wasn't able to sleep. He answered her call, late as it was, as though it were an every early hour occurrence, the warmth and desire in his voice apparent, almost as though in imagination she stood at his hand. Her news quickly restored him to his normal condition. Standing by the phone, he almost recoiled in dismay, if initially, for his own sake and the sake of the play, then, immediately regretting his moment of selfishness, tried to make amends by assuring her he would handle everything. He knew very well Katia's devotion to her mother and he was, in his own way, shaken by her news, all the more so because Carole McCabe was still an attractive and vital woman.

In the end it was settled, even if Katia was left with the faint impression that Ivor hoped the trip was not going to develop into more than an extended bedside visit to reassure herself that her mother was in good hands. In any case, Ivor promised to write every day and Katia knew this was no idle promise, because writing for Ivor, in any form, was a compulsion. He had even been known to scribble all over tablecloths, for only by the written word did he spring to full life.

Afterwards, it took Katia the best part of an hour to pack what she considered she would need on the trip and prepare for bed. Her head ached terribly, but automatically, from long habit, she stood in front of the mirror and brushed her hair, staring sightlessly at her white face, a frail flower in the wind in her white nightdress. Her mouth went askew and a torrent of tears sprang to her eyes, hot and hopeless to control for a long while. This time tomorrow night she would be on Carunya, and what of her mother? How would she find her?

Suddenly her mother's affliction seemed too much to bear, so real and so close to her she could feel the pain herself. In that moment she would willingly have taken on all suffering herself. She flung the brush away from her and hopped into bed, pulling the clothes over her head in an excess of misery, curling her fists into the palms of her hands in her distress. But there was no shelter from the realities of life. She had to take stock of herself. Her mother was a realist. She knew what life was about. If her mother could fight back from adversity so could she. Life wasn't for the sawdust people who buried their heads. As soon as one admitted defeat, it was time to give up.

Thinking this, her eyes flew open and she pushed out from under the blankets. 'Never give in' was the first rule of life. Never mind being a success. She couldn't care less about that. Through her open windows came a celebration of stars, so beautiful and benign, tremendously reassuring, glittering on her doorstep, a true Fontainebleau white, the purest of diamonds. She might almost have touched them had she got out of bed.

Her breath quivered on the quiet air and she closed her eyes again. The mind and the will to survive had worked miracles in the past. They would again. And there was always Thorn. And hope. Exhausted, she fell into a deep sleep, and all the while Carunya waited for her like a slumbering giant.

CHAPTER THREE

THE glare of the Outback! The heat and the heart-stopping vastness; the taste of dust in the mouth. Katia stared down at the harsh, red-ochre landscape, wild, scrubby country, deeply indented, scored and wrinkled with a maze of dried-up natural irrigation channels that could run in the Wet fifty miles wide. To the east and the west and the centre stretched the limitless plains of saltbush, the spinifex and the mallee; the great belt of salt lakes, the glaring, barren immensity of the desert. Mirage country where one could easily die.

The great wedge-tailed eagles flew beneath them, mere black specks in the blazing blue air, soaring on the down wind, while the Piper rode smoothly through the vast, brassy dome, homing on in to its destination – Carunya. Dressed in a thin shirt and flared slacks, Katia looked as neat as a pageboy, her small high-cheekboned face very serious, almost fatalistic. Her whole being seemed flooded with white-hot light that pricked at her long graceful neck and broke out on a fine dew at her nape and her temples. Beside her at the controls, Thorn was silent, black, heavy-lidded eyes narrowed against the pitiless glare. Carunya was not so many miles distant and she knew he could hardly wait to be there. No rewards, no inducements, no public honours could keep Thorn long from his own seat of power. Any separation was in the nature of an endurance test. Feeling her eyes on him, he turned to smile at her, sophisticated and devious, but regarding her steadily.

'A martyr on the rack with a look of absolute tragedy on her face! Don't do it, little one. Everything's going to be all right.'

'I hope so, Thorn. Oh, I do hope so!' she whispered back.

'I've made you a promise!' He brushed her hand briefly with miracles of dynamism. 'Sooner or later you'll have to learn to relax that nervous system. Take a deep breath and fill your lungs with the scents of the land.'

'I can't!' she said seriously. 'There's heat everywhere, glittery eyes, birds and lizards and great sinewy animals and trees that crouch and wait to pull you into the shadows!'

'Such imagination!' he half smiled. 'I'm glad you've grown out of all your old antics. Or have you?'

She shrugged and moved her eyes from his dark profile to the earth beneath. The first torrid red line of sandhills were coming up. 'McCabe's Kingdom!' she said with a funny touch of irony. 'It moves inexorably over all of us. It's your whole existence. I want to escape it, yet somehow I can't. The fierce seasons, the heat, the bizarre, strutting colours. The legions of cattle, the cloud castles, the spirit of the bush. Corroboree and dawn rituals and inhuman chants. And those lovely curving mahogany banisters. Why use the stairs? The house.'

He laughed softly and she turned on him, lifting her head with a nervous, sensitive look, like a young filly. 'Why are you laughing?'

'You. Just you. You've always been able to make me

laugh. Leggy little Katia, some emissary from an elfin court, trailing the promise of beauty and a whole battery of mystifying moods. You know, Kat, in a lot of ways you're every bit as untamed as that desert down there, and just as lonely. Too much sensitivity is bad for survival. I thought I got through to you on that.'

'You've done your best to toughen me up. Perhaps I wasn't such a good pupil, though I couldn't count the number of times I've sat at your feet.' Two identical tears formed in her eyes and slid down her cheeks.

'Stop that!' he said briskly. 'That's not the way, Katia. That's not the way at all!'

'I'm so worried about Mother!' She made a valiant attempt to recover herself and wiped the tears away with the back of her hand.

'I'm worried about her too, but it won't help to show it so badly.'

'I'm sorry. I know. I'll be quite different at the house,' she said, and her voice brightened with irony. 'You'll see. I'm a very good actress.'

A curiously withdrawn expression came into his eyes that puzzled her. 'Yes, you are, and that's not all you are, is it, Katia?'

The look might have baffled her, but his next words were familiar enough. 'It's always *the house*, isn't it?' he said in a cool, appraising voice. 'Right from the start. Never *home*. Where did we go wrong, I wonder? The children fit the pattern so perfectly.'

'They're McCabes, of course.' Her hand moved over her hair and he was aware of the tension in her. 'They didn't have to develop the style or the manner. It was a natural heritage. God-given, what else? The reason why they've been so completely accepted by the whole

42

clan, for all my mother was an outsider. The reason I wasn't. *Ever!*'

His eyes were brilliantly clear, his hard, lean body as resilient as a whip. 'Remember we didn't suit you either, honey lamb!'

'*You* did. A black McCabe, illustrious heir to the throne. The whole set-up is quite feudal out here. Maggie was always my enemy.'

'Oh, come now!' he said quietly, with a serious undertone. 'Maggie never understood you, Katia, and you were quite a handful. I seem to remember spending a great deal of time saving you from yourself. Do you wonder Maggie who's so forthright could ever fathom you out? She was never deliberately unkind to you, was she?'

'No, of course not!' she said, barely able to keep the tremor out of her voice. Maggie, far from being forthright, had been enormously subtle in her dealings with her new-found niece, so that even Thorn, so searching and able to look beneath the surface, had been unable to find fault with her, even if privately he regretted her lack of warm friendliness. Right from the start, Maggie had succeeded in creating the illusion of trying to give of her best in a difficult situation. There had been no doubt in anyone's mind that the young Katia had taken her father's death badly. Her mother's sudden and never anticipated remarriage had taken Katia by storm. It shocked her, making it difficult for her to give her mother her blessing, let alone adjust to a whole new way of life. Her mother's people were not her people, for all they wanted to make her over lock, stock and barrel.

So Maggie had been subtle. She liked it that way. It

gave her enormous solitary pleasure, for no one, not even her own brother, had ever credited her with such a thing. But Katia knew and Maggie knew that no other man's child would be allowed to slip into a position of belonging. Outsiders were outsiders and they always had been. No money. No breeding, for all Katia's remarked-upon beauty. Not even a name. Her mother had been luckier, secure in Charles' love and protection. A child could not hope to be nearly so fortunate.

The whole business didn't bear thinking about, yet it echoed over and over like a bad dream. Maggie liked judging character, then sitting in judgment. She saw herself as a woman with whom it was impossible to pretend, a fair-minded woman but impossible to flatter or win over or earn her good will. She would allow no frivolity to temper her decisions, and she made a great deal of them. She was *Miss McCabe* of Carunya, a member of a great pioneering family with power and influence and far-reaching interests. *Money spoke all languages,* Maggie was fond of declaiming, like an old-time orator, drawing Katia's fiery: 'Hang your lousy money!' as a child.

She had been paying for that ever since. A woman like Maggie considered herself beyond retaliation. It was one of her peculiarities. From her father and her grandfather she had culled mannerisms and traits of behaviour, digestible in the male line when allied to their dynamic qualities but very hard to take in Miss Maggie McCabe who had all their iron but none of their humour and fire.

'She's a witch! A real witch! I could kill her!' Katia had stormed at her mother, and saw horror and sympathy in her mother's fine eyes but no real belief. Carole had long since written off her formidable sister-in-law as an 'awful old bitch', but she couldn't allow Katia the witching qualities, for she had never seen them, and she spent a great deal of time and stealth looking. But whatever Maggie was, she found it a simple enough matter to flaw Katia's years on Carunya and she accomplished it a great deal easier than most. So the upsets and the arguments, the tempers and tantrums had changed nothing. It had been a private war, privately waged, and Katia had the sickening notion that it was doomed to go on for ever. Maggie would never be able to stop herself going sour, even if the years had persuaded her to accept Katia's mother. After all, she *was* Charles' widow and the mother of his two youngest children, both of whom received a mention in Maggie's will.

Katia tried to shake off her thoughts. They were too painful to probe anyway. It was easier by far not to dwell on Maggie McCabe and her elaborate and various methods for retaining mastery. It was a mania with her. She should really have been a general. It was even possible, Katia reflected, for some people to so get a stranglehold on others' lives that there seemed no escape from them save in death. She swung her black hair, trying to rid herself of her dismal thoughts, and turned her head to encounter Thorn's narrowed stare.

'Well? Are you coming out of your trance? I'm prepared to hear the worst. You've taken long enough to consider.'

She made a little awkward movement. 'Oh no, no!' How could she turn Thorn against the aunt who

45

worshipped the ground he walked upon? 'I know it sounds odd, but don't you judge me, Thorn. Don't think about me at all!'

Trained as she was to listen intently to the sound of her own voice, she heard its delicate pathos. Her eyes were enormous, the pupils enlarged by tension, more dark blue than black, twin diamond points at the centre. He gave her a faint, pitying smile that stirred her to a restless energy, an urgency to be physically active.

'Old habits die hard, jewel-flower. You're the one person who's ever made me uneasy, but there's no need to sound as if it matters terribly. The thing is, it would be impossible not to think of you as well, you know.'

Katia didn't laugh or make a flippant comment. 'Would it?' she said very simply.

'Yes!' His eyes seemed to be challenging her, leading her deeper and deeper into some swirling labyrinth as dark as his eyes. And that was Thorn's way. She had a quick moment of breathlessness, a draining of confidence such as she experienced the minute before a rising curtain. Never look afraid when you are afraid, she thought, and tilted her head on its slender neck with enchanting aloofness. He caught the look and his expression relaxed.

'Beautiful, Kat!' There was laughter in his easy, disturbing voice. 'An enchantress so desperately uncertain of herself!'

The slow, gentle drawl restored her to ease again. 'Oh, you're a savage,' she said, and looked into his guarded, dark face. 'Prince of barbaric practices. You excel at this cat-and-mouse game.'

'Compose yourself!' he said, and laughed, his eyes

46

sweeping her face. 'You've got a few gambits yourself!'

'Ah, but yours are deliberate, aren't they? Though it's impossible to pinpoint your motives for anything. You don't fit into a type or a pattern. It's frustrating, but fascinating too. Even as a child you set out to assail my stubborn little mind.'

'But you always meant to surrender, didn't you, Kat?' There was a slight, rough edge to his voice, a difference in him that made her want to keep retreating to new strategic positions. Thorn always swung the pendulum between rapture and rage. With a leap of the imagination she crossed the years, a hundred remembrances fresh in her, yet she seemed to be two separate persons, or the Thorn she knew so well was.

'Oh, lord!' she said, and dropped her face into her hands, her black hair swinging like a bell. 'Have pity, Thorn. I'm not nearly as knowledgeable and sophisticated as I appear!'

'I'm damned glad you're not, but you are a little crazy. Tell me about d'Arcy.'

'I won't!' she said, surviving a panic moment.

'Why not? I might be able to give you a few tips.'

'I don't need any, thank you!' she said rapidly.

'How right you are!' He turned his head to smile at her, his shapely mouth wry. 'In fact, you could turn a man violent! But seriously, Katia, you wanted your chance and I saw you got it. Your own ability did the rest. Maggie, or anyone else for that matter, hasn't a hope in hell of upsetting your applecart. You don't need me to tell you any more. Just keep saying it to yourself, over and over.'

She suddenly shivered and his eyes flickered her face.

'What's the matter?'

'Nothing. Forget it, Big Brother!'

The explanation was received with an expressive silence and the tilt of one black brow. 'I know you so well, yet I seem to be slipping into some new dimension where I don't know you at all,' she said a shade fretfully.

He laughed in his throat, a beam of sunlight falling across his handsome, dark face. 'Of course you don't,' he said convincingly. 'I think I have a claustrophobic effect on you, Kat.'

'Oh, don't be absurd!'

'I'm not being absurd,' he pointed out dryly. 'It's pointless to deny it. Your face mirrors every emotion — didn't you know?'

'I don't want to know, perhaps!' Swiftly she lowered her heavy dark lashes. 'Talk to me about the tsetse fly or something.'

'Not yet. Look at me, Kat, don't hang your head!'

She coloured a little and angled her head sideways, her hair clouding her face. He met her brilliant blue gaze. Flower-sapphires, her mouth parted.

'Poor little Kat!' he said, his own eyes glinting. 'Don't ever hate me, darling. Don't ever!'

She trembled convulsively, pain in the twist of her exquisitely shaped mouth. 'How could you say such a ghastly thing?'

His hand shot out to grasp her wrist. 'Maybe even I need a little reassurance therapy from time to time. Forget it, baby, it's been hell lately.' He made a grimace and shrugged his wide shoulders, releasing her hand. 'There are so many things tied up with your childhood, something in you that strenuously resist the McCabes. I'm a McCabe.'

'You *are* McCabe!' she said oddly, her mind full of old thoughts.

'Well, don't fret,' he flicked her a leashed look. 'You shall have your cake and eat it too. Home and children yet. So dry up your sticky sweet tears. It's a success, not a sob-story. I promised you that.'

'But I don't think I want it!' she said, a mixture of a dozen muddled emotions wanting her to contradict herself.

He flickered her a brief look without turning his head, some nuance in his voice giving his words uncomfortable depth.

'Do you think it an advantage to be so inconsistent, Kat, or can't you help it?'

'I'm a woman!'

'A dire warning, and don't look for any fancied affronts. It would be a nice idea to put you in a cage and not let anyone else near you, but it wouldn't work out, I'm afraid. Quicksilver Kat!' He smiled at her, knowledge in his slanting black eyes, and she seemed to come alive with a million sensations. They had shared so much of the past, it seemed as if he would dominate the pattern of the years. Thorn had always cut away pretences between them, so there was no point in acting.

'I feel giddy and feverish!' she said with all her old nervous impatience.

'Reaction. Always in proportion to the amount of nervous energy you put out. Yet the kids are placid young things.'

49

'Maggie must take great pride in them,' she said, her beautiful dark blue eyes untroubled in that moment by her own rejection.

'She does. You were a total escape, but I've always liked you. You're a rainbow shot through with colours and a rainbow I could live with for ever. If you go off and marry Don Giovanni I'll be bitterly disappointed.'

'Ivor is a very distinguished playwright!' she said repressively, trying to draw him off.

'A household word, no less. I'm not criticizing, honey lamb, that would be a piece of arrant stupidity. It would set you off headlong in his defence. You like to build a maze around yourself, but in this case it's not necessary. I'm longing to meet Ivor, in fact as soon as Carole shows steady progress we'll have him out. He rides, of course?'

'Oh, shut up!' she said a little breathlessly. 'You're not going to shatter me, though you were never a man like other men, you phenomenal creature!'

'Poor little Kat!' he drawled, looking down his straight nose at her. 'Don't make things worse for yourself.'

'You and your threats!' She glanced at him fleetingly, then away again. It seemed much safer that way. 'I don't think Ivor does ride, actually.'

'Tut, tut!' his eyes gleamed and his mouth twisted with obvious amusement. 'One can't have everything, and there *is* an element of danger in life on the land. Does Ivor like danger? *You* do, or rather you're drawn to it!'

She turned her head to him meeting the cool, level gaze. 'It's the greatest mistake to encourage you,

Thorn. I'll learn.'

'Will you now?' The air suddenly seemed static, in a few words setting them adrift in a barbarous landscape. 'I always hold the whip hand, Katy darling, and it's damned presumption on your part to expect anything else.'

'I'm sorry!' She inclined her dark head and the black line of her hair arced across her flushed cheeks.

'You look like a ruffled rose!' he observed lightly. 'No, *I'm* sorry, I keep wanting to test out a theory of mine.'

'About me?'

'About no one else!' There was a mocking, amused timbre in his dark, resonant voice. 'But to come down to less exhausting matters, for all the kids were born in the saddle they don't ride half as well as you. You've got the gift – a natural. I don't think I even had to tell you how to sit, let alone hold the reins. Pretty extraordinary when you consider you'd never been within a few hundred yards of a horse. I can still see you, enormous blue eyes, moody as blazes, melting into love for an Arab stallion.'

'They made life bearable for me, the horses. A whole new existence!'

'Oh, don't talk nonsense!' he chopped her off rather brutally. 'You had plenty of good times on Carunya, but you've always had this melodramatic bent. Why don't you damned well admit it? There were good times on Carunya, weren't there, Kat, you stubborn little mule?'

Tensions were building up between them, but they were irretrievably linked. The thought of Maggie's silent maliciousness caused a shadow of withdrawal to flit across her face, enhancing the poignant look that only made his own face harden.

'Deserts of silence!' he said tersely, pinning her gaze.

Her breath caught and she turned away with soft urgency. 'Of course there were!' She looked down at the sandhills with trance-like concentration. 'But I made so many mistakes. So many!'

'Stop punishing yourself!' he said, his head turned away from her slender fragility, 'and don't hold on to memories that are best forgotten. You're all grown up now, though it's impossible not to think of you as you were as a child.'

'And you never change either!' she said with an acute desire to ruffle his steely composure.

The brilliant black eyes only sparkled with interest. 'I agree. Aren't you lucky?'

'And there's no question of my being nice to you either!'

'You'll be as I want you to be!' he said with the merest lick of a threat in his voice, arrogance implicit in his lean, powerful frame. 'So rid yourself of any other idea.'

'Perhaps I won't!' she said, not surrendering to the blaze of power. 'Perhaps I've grown tired of a child-hood forever following you.'

'Ah, mutiny!' he said, and laughed. So relaxed, so assured so untroubled by all of her different moods, that the moment of tension was dispelled between them. 'Exciting, isn't it? The idea of crossing swords with your enemy, McCabe.' He looked across at her and caught the unguarded expression in her shimmering, deeply blue eyes. 'All right, what does that mean, the jewel-bright expression?'

Katia gave a curious, rapid shake of her head, prepared but not proof against the swift arrogant charm of a very white smile. 'Don't make things more difficult for me, Thorn.'

His voice was amused but emphatic. '*You* were always the one for fanciful nonsense. But sit back and relax!'

'Would I waste time arguing with the king of the castle!'

He stared at her for a moment as if trying to decipher every thought in her head, then he said in a deep drawl:

'I'll remember that piece of intentional insolence. Terribly careless, Kat. The time may have come when I'm going to hold you responsible for your actions!'

'Very wise, I'm sure!' she said, raising her eyebrows slightly.

'*Inevitable*, that's the word, Katia Grenville.'

Beneath the suave mask was a smile, and a surge of feeling shot through her stronger than her own will, holding her fast in its shocking turbulence. It came to her suddenly that she had a deep-seated resistance to Thorn, like a bid for survival, but it didn't seem possible. Her feelings for him were too strong and too complex to ever drive out. Realization struck her, and her white skin turned even whiter.

With that special awareness he had, he turned his dark head to her with its quality of rock-hard masculinity.

'Look down at Carunya, little one. Don't let it overwhelm you. There's no fear or dread down there. There's your mother who loves you and the children who never tire of keeping up their scrapbook on their beautiful stepsister. You're no stranger knocking on the wrong door. Carunya is mine and you don't even have to smile at me to gain an entrance!'

The wave of feeling that hit Katia was so immense she didn't even know how to control it. She stared down at the stark magnificence beneath her un- seeingly, her whole being fraught with impending up- heaval. The heat and the sunbaked landscape slipped away to the edge of the world. The river ran between the high red cliffs, glittering and flashing like a ribbon of precious stones. The air-strip was a mile distant and she could see the ring of white buildings guarding the Big House, the white master's retreat.

Someone was tearing down the rough track, driving a truck with all the careless skill and abandon of a station hand, one hand on the wheel, one circling and waving his broad-brimmed hat. From the look on Thorn's face, the pride of possession, he couldn't wait to put down soon enough, yet she had never felt more unsettled or lost. But why judge herself or make com- parisons? she thought, bitter-sweet. She could never hope to measure herself against Thorn or ever kill her feeling for him.

The shadow of the Piper raced along the land while the plane made its descent on a beam of sunlight. Trees and scrub sprang to life, the leaves catching the light turning to points of flame. Birds came up from the billabongs in a multi-coloured cloud and the sudden flash of the sun on the dipping wing was like an explo- sion of light.

There beneath them, with its great roof glittering like mica in the white-hot sun, was the homestead –

Carunya. Katia tensed in her seat, the safety belt cutting into her narrow waist. The Piper hit a pocket above the sandhill at the approach to the strip, then sailed right in. The outbuildings flashed past the windows, the wheels touched down, they were slowing. Thorn was home. She was back!

CHAPTER FOUR

CAROLE lay in the great canopied bed she had come to as Charles' wife. Susan and Debra had been born there. Charles, the beloved, the irreplaceable, had died there. It only seemed yesterday since, distraught and bewildered, she had watched Thorn and Mike Conlon carry him in. Charles, the unconquerable, a man of great strength, had been beaten by one savage, unheralded heart attack. The shock and the unspeakable grief of it had hit her harder than anything she had ever borne, making her own illness seem unremarkable.

His dressing gown still hung in the large, roomy closet. She often wore it, though it hung in voluminous folds around her. Some part of her dear, dear Charles, though Maggie deplored what she saw as excessive morbidity. Maggie didn't believe in indulging human weaknesses, though no one could have been more unswervingly loyal to her brother, or more stonily heartbroken at his death. *Loyalty*. A powerful factor in my final acceptance as Charles' widow, Carole thought, and thinking this, her mind sped to her daughter Katia, of all her children, the one least like her and the one that came closest to her heart. Katia, her dazzling daughter, so gifted and unpredictable. What a funny little girl she had been!

Sunlight streamed through the room, touching the beautiful furnishings, the richly textured design on the circular rug, the serene white walls, the cool, stripped oak floor, the green and white of the fern-printed bed-spread. Thorn had turned her bed, so she had a two-sided view of the restrained 'wilderness' of blossoming native trees and shrubs, and beyond the silvery sum-mery beauty of the Lily Lagoon.

Carole simply lay there, isolated by her illness with only her 'voices' to speak to her. She lay quietly gather-ing strength, not allowing herself a sense of recoil in her own disability, for she was a woman of character and discipline. She had only gratitude for the fact that her speech and her face had not been affected, and as for the rest, she would put up a good fight. Deliberately she went back over snatches of her life that had brought her happiness and peace.

. . . The early days with Shawn, when he had been so gay and vital, ready to startle the world with his multi-faceted talents, for he could paint as well. Shawn pacing about their tiny living-room, the furniture not fully paid for, going over and over his lines, in his never-ending search for perfection, chiding her with sometimes real and sometimes mock irritation when she fell asleep or fed him lines 'like a limp fish'. Shawn, and his pride and relief at being presented with their beautiful daughter Katia. Even as an hour-old infant her resemblance to Shawn had been startling, laugh-able really.

Lying there, with no real strength or wish to read, Carole coloured her day with her remembrances. The night was the worst. The lonely dark hours when her recumbent body felt as heavy as lead and she couldn't help remembering that Charles had always said she had the figure of a girl. It was as well he had gone first, for he would have been greatly distressed by her handicap, not for his own, but for her sake. *Charles!* Her heart still beat like a girl's. The years they had together had been few, but with tremendous quality, which was the best way to judge time.

Thinking about Charles, she had many little guilty stabs about Shawn. He had been her first love, her young love, and she deeply regretted that she had not loved him entirely. Shawn had always been that bit beyond her reach. They never fully shared their enthusiasms, their hopes or dreams. Charles had been her own from the first moment she had turned and met his visionary blue eyes. She, who had no life outside her daughter or ever thought to marry again, had met and married the wealthy and influential Charles McCabe through sheer chance, the element that governed all forms of life.

Hurrying frantically through her shopping so she could collect Katia from school on time, she had stepped out precipitately from the kerb and almost under a car. The car had been Charles'. Her shining white knight — and he *had* been that, for all they laughed about it afterwards. Charles had brought fulfilment into her life when she thought it had missed her for ever. Tears, not unhappy tears, slid out of her eyes and oozed gently on to the pillow. She brought up her good hand and wiped her face stealthily. Soon Sarah, Nurse Walker, would come in, full of kindness and good humour, but sometimes Carole couldn't help resenting the invasions on her privacy. She had to remind herself that resentment was futile, self-defeating.

She wasn't as she used to be, whole and strong, unthinkingly able to control her own body. Her paralysis, though slight, weighed heavily on her. It was beastly really, but she fully intended to do something about it. She clung to this, not with desperation, but a firm hope. Charles had taught her that – the power of the human will to win out in the end. She couldn't fail him or her children, or Thorn whom she had come to love as her own son. Thorn was bringing Kat home again. The tears still gathered and she blinked them back. She was excited, that was it, though she had best control it, in case it came against her. Today her Katia would be beside her, brilliant blue eyes probably swimming with tears, for Kat had the tenderest heart in the world and never troubled to hide it from her mother. A faint nausea which had niggled her all night suddenly subsided and Carole fully relaxed.

If only she could see Katia married to a good man who would love and best of all understand her. She would never have a financial worry. Charles had settled a considerable sum on her which she would receive when she turned twenty-five. Katia still didn't know this, only that she would be handed an envelope with a letter from Charles to be read on the morning of her twenty-fifth birthday. Charles had tried so hard with Kat, but the child had stubbornly resisted him because of her blind loyalty to her own father, but she had placed her young life in his son's hands.

Thorn. What would they have done without him? She could never have coped on her own, for there had been all sorts of problems and Charles so busy from dawn to dusk, but she could never say she had not been forewarned, knowing Shawn and the legacy of his temperament. Not that Shawn had given much time to his small daughter for all he was proud of her. But he had *been* there, with all his vivid exuberance and his creative silences.

It was Thorn who had worked a small miracle with Kat. Thorn and his horses. Strange for a city-bred child like Kat to have taken to them with such enormous devotion, an intense joy in their beauty and flowing movement. It was almost as Thorn said, Katia had been born to live with horses. Katia, as exquisite as a small figurine, deceptively fragile, one glossy black pigtail hanging down her back, never a hat, perched on the back of almost anything in the stable except Thorn's big black stallion, Rimfire, and only then because he had threatened to break her neck if she ever attempted to ride it. She never had, which said a great deal for Thorn's power over her, for the young Kat would have attempted to ride anything, hardly able to contain her energy, vibrant with life and excitement, racing about the property, until she came face to face with Maggie, then ... silence and withdrawal, and sometimes quite suddenly and unpredictably, ungovernable childish rages, when nothing save Thorn's dark-shaded voice and his easy way of ignoring or checking her worst tantrum seemed to soothe her. He simply knew how to handle her even at the times when her own mother couldn't reach her and she too felt like subsiding in tears. To Thorn, Katia was no more than a little, elegant, high-strung filly, and he left it at that.

Maggie was too stiff, too self-righteous and reserved with such a dry-as-bleached-bones manner to ever appeal to a child. Or an adult, for that matter. Indeed, it had been hard for Carole to credit that she was Charles's sister, except for the strong family resemblance. Charles, like his son and his two small daughters, possessed a deep vein of humour, a very real charm that made Carole think they had unfairly grabbed the lot. Maggie was Maggie and there wasn't much anyone could do about it, for she fully intended to live out her life like a queen on Carunya and Carole had never had the heart to suggest otherwise – not that Charles had ever mentioned it. Charles had taken everything in his stride, the good and the bad, so they all lived with Maggie and made the best of it. Certainly she had mellowed with the years to the extent that she had learnt to unbend with Susan and Debby.

It was Katia who had been treated to the civil and off-putting indifference Maggie reserved for strangers, or outsiders, as she liked to call them. Maggie McCabe, Carole thought, and sighed. A hard, unsentimental woman. Perhaps if she had married and had children of her own her nature would have been softened or equally well, she might have made her own children's lives a quiet misery with her high and rather unreasonable demands.

Almost for a moment Carole started. *Misery?* Now why had she thought of that? Katia, of course. Kat had always been violent and voluble about Maggie as if her own young life had been made a kind of hell away from Thorn and her beloved horses, yet she had searched and searched for some hidden flaw in Maggie's treatment of her daughter and found none, until, unhappy and distressed, Carole had been forced back on Charles's theory: Katia had found adjustment to her new life painful and overwhelming. The little wild one, Charles had nicknamed her, and all too often it had proved true, until Thorn had taken over and tamed her like a bird in the hand.

The soft pad of footsteps sounded along the corridor,

and in another minute Nurse Walker came through the door, her pleasant suntanned face kind and alert grey eyes penetrating, quietly self-assured. Sarah Walker was a good nurse and she knew it, making of it her life's work. Her uniform smelled clean and fresh and she came to stand beside Carole's bed, looking down at her as she spoke.

'Your morning tea will be up in a minute or so, Mrs. McCabe. Such activity downstairs! Royalty, no less. I never thought it possible for a house as beautiful as this one to look even better, but this morning it rates the centre page in *Home Decorating*. Flowers everywhere. Young Minnie's to have all the credit. She gathered them and arranged them and very artistically too. Yet you could never say a white woman did them. There's just that little touch of the unexpected – a combination of this and that we never think of ourselves. I must say I like it. She's a clever little thing, Minnie, and so deft about the house, not like the new little one, what's her name, Josie. Goodness, the near misses I've had with her, and she will turn the floors into a skating rink! Everything so beautiful, and all for your daughter!' As she spoke, she moved about, methodically checking Carole's progress and marking up the chart for Dr. Armstrong who was due in the following afternoon. After a little while she gazed back thoughtfully at Carole, a professional face watching her, then she smiled, completely at ease. 'We'll take good care of you, Mrs. McCabe, with plenty of good signs to hold on to!'

Reassured, for all her calm demeanour, Carole returned the smile. 'You're a nice woman, Sarah, and a credit to your profession!'

A faint blush mantled Sarah's tanned cheeks and she fell to straightening the already impeccable bed. 'I like you too, Mrs. McCabe, and I admire you. It's not easy to have the right attitude right from the start and it will count for a lot, you'll see. In fact, between the two of us, we're going to get you mobile again in double quick time!' She turned and opened out the windows and the breeze stroked the long filmy curtains. The flowers came closer, bringing fragrant memories of days scarcely past when Carole had tended the beds, weeding out the summer profusion of weeds. How long before she could work in her garden again? Such an enriching experience to bring forth from the soil a whole range of flowers and plants, her countless lovely azaleas and camellias, the wisteria she had trained to climb over the upstairs balcony, a glorious tumbling mass of blossom, her bonsai willows raised from cuttings taken in the early spring just before Debby had been born. She was very proud of them with their wonderfully aged effect and attractive shape. She had not been nearly so successful with the Japanese maples. Her garden had become an addiction, especially since Charles died, but the resultant effect was sheer magic, even if she said it herself. The lawns and the beautifully trimmed evergreens and citrus trees she left to the boys but the flowers and shrubs were her own. Two acres of beautiful sequestered semi-bushland that sloped away to the Lily Lagoon, incomparably lovely when floating its canopy of lotus flowers.

With a little start of surprise Carole came back to the sound of Sarah's pleasant, unhurried voice.

'. . . It will be wonderful to have her back again. The girls have shown me their scrapbook. They're very proud of her. She certainly is beautiful. Very unusual too. So many good-looking girls tend to look alike – copy their favourite film star, I expect!'

A special emotion touched Carole's voice and she smoothed the daisy-sprigged sheet under her slack hand. 'I've always thought of my eldest daughter as a spicy carnation. I love flowers, you know. My other two are chrysanthemums, but Katia is different, exotic. Yet the first thing I remember when I came out of the clouds of that first difficult birth was the doctor saying: "Well, young woman, I surely don't understand it, but I've delivered a rose, a perfect pink rose, and I'm positive I'll never do it again!" You can't imagine, Sarah, how full of pride and importance I was. Shawn named her. I thought it such an odd name at the time and really I wanted to name her after my own mother, Elizabeth, but there you are! She's Katia, just as Shawn wanted it, and I must say it suits her. Thorn was the one to start calling her Kat and I've fallen into the same habit, so have the little girls. If I shut my eyes I can picture her standing beside the bed, anxious and loving and perhaps even frightened I might suffer some new stroke – but we won't talk about that!'

'We won't let it happen, you mean!' Sarah said with a fierceness of emotion that surprised herself. 'Now, here's your cuppa!'

Carole turned her head and let her eyes travel past Sarah's tall, straight figure to see Minnie's small dusky face with its glistening eyes and irregular features, her mouth slightly parted over perfect white teeth as if in awe and anticipation, almost visibly holding her breath. Carole almost smiled in wry amusement. This constant anxious inspection by the entire household!

She'd even caught Thorn out once or twice and he'd grinned at her in quick recognition with that teasing evocative glimpse of Charles, though Thorn was a 'black' McCabe and there was only one of those every so often. Charles had been as fair as herself, and Susan and Debby were blue-eyed blondes with enviable complexions that took the sun.

'Thank you, Minnie,' Carole said in a clear, strong voice, and purposefully so. 'You're a good, thoughtful child!'

Minnie faintly giggled and lifted her curly head a fraction, heartened by the matter-of-fact voice from the bed. The Missus was herself again! The black eyes touched Carole very lightly as if she was to be cosseted very carefully; a solitary golden bush that might never flower again, Carole thought fancifully. But too much cosseting was just as bad for flowers as it was for human beings. She twisted in the bed, her lips tightening, the only sign she made of her unprecedented physical disability.

'Miss Walker has just been telling me you arranged the flowers, Minnie, and all so beautifully,' she continued, and watched the pleasure and eagerness leap into the glossy eyes.

'For Miss Kate!' Minnie supplied shyly, though she had only met Katia once since she had been sent from the Mission Station to work at the house, quite an honour for a well-trained girl. Softly and totally anxious to please, Minnie added, 'I haven't finished yours yet, Miz McCabe, but I'm going to bring up such a vase, you'll see!' Then she broke off and stood seemingly mesmerized until Sarah kindly helped her out, winking at her:

'Good girl! You go downstairs and go to it. I'll bring Mrs. McCabe's tray down.'

The voice of pleasant authority quickly dispatched Minnie and both women watched her back out of the room very softly, rather blindly as a child might, then smoothly and efficiently Sarah propped up her patient against the pillows and settled the tray across her knees, not making any further attempt to offer assistance.

A refreshing bit of common sense and understanding, Carole thought, and lifted her delicate teacup quite steadily with her good hand, sipping at the hot, fragrant tea. She knew inside her a rising sense of elation. Soon Katia would be here and they would talk of many things and she could forget for a time that she was reduced a little. Not her true self, her soul or her being, but the dependent physical side of herself.

As though thought-reading, which she was, and trained to it, Sarah's pleasantly plain face creased into a quick, comforting smile, a promise that one day Carole would be restored to a lot of her old vigour. And I couldn't hope for more than that, Carole thought, and even then it would be enough! She had lived a good life and it wasn't over yet. Because she was human, a faint sense of pathos stabbed at her, a flicker of why should it be, but she dismissed it almost as soon as it touched her, allowing no bitterness to intrude. Bitterness was corrosive, eating away all that was fine in one, coming between what one was and what one wished to be.

Sarah, wise and always willing, suddenly launched into some hilarious incidents from her trainee days and soon both women were touched with the grace-note of laughter, the great healer.

Across the runway Debby, half a head shorter than Susan, broke out like a welcome flag, dancing wildly in front of the slowing Piper. Flanking her, their glossy tails streaking, came Remus and Rom, Thorn's two beautiful red setters. They made a lovely moving picture, and Katia smiled but waved her small welcome party back off the runway, conscious that Thorn was swearing mildly under his breath, flinging up an admonishing hand, for once jolted out of his supreme self-possession.

'Damned little goat! That's the last of that kind of antic!' His brilliant black gaze, hard as the gaze of an idol, fell on Debby's momentarily bent and repentant head. She had fallen back well clear of the light aircraft calling the two prancing, over-excited dogs to attention. Thorn's fine, shapely mouth set in lines of amusement. 'The contrition won't last long. Full of bubbles, that's Debby.'

'The friendliest little soul in the world, and so very endearing! She's the most like Mother of all of us. I hope you're not going to scold her, she wasn't all that close!'

'Close enough!' Thorn cut her off with little concession. 'There's always danger in that kind of thing. Kids will do anything when they're excited.'

Outside the window, her high spirits on the ascent again, Debby seemed bent on precipitating herself through the unopened door, her clear silvery voice floating on the breeze.

'Greetings, greetings, O beauteous one! Hello there, brother Thorn!'

Behind Debby came Susan, a cooler, more determined version of her sister, far more critical and sparing with her approval, but in this case, her fine-boned small face wreathed in smiles.

'Katy! Katy, you're doing your hair differently. It's dazzling!'

'Dazzling!' Thorn repeated with the kind of good-humoured irony that was so attractive. 'It's affected me too, Kat, but not perhaps quite in the same way!' The familiar, fathomless eyes lightly flicked Katia's face and he leaned over and released her seat belt, taxiing the sleek Cherokee Six towards the hangar and the waiting attendant. The sun struck like flame over the mould of his cheekbones, the polished, darkly tanned skin, the veiled lids. He looked so strong and unassailable. Challenging, exasperating, and sometimes downright hurtful.

Thinking this, she gave a faint sigh, and he looked back at her swiftly, the black eyes arrogant, interrogating.

'What is it this time, Kat? Though I know I should be used to all your strange and delicate little reticences!'

She continued to stare at him, her fringed eyes distended, glowing like sapphires between the tips of her thick, open lashes.

'Won't answer. Can't answer. Which?' His hard mouth set in contradictory lines of mockery and amusement. 'Whatever it is, it's struck a vibrating chord!'

A sparkling kind of tension united them, like frosting on glass, and she sighed again, her breath escaping through her parted, rose-tinted mouth. 'Even I can't explain it!' she said quite truthfully. 'Unasked, unwanted, unwelcome me as ever, except for my very own!'

68

'Rubbish!' His voice jolted her right out of her dream state. 'You just like tormenting yourself. And me, into the bargain. God knows I've done my very best to make Carunya as much like home for you as I can. This is no time for histrionics, Kat!'

'I know. I know!' she said, trying to placate him. It was never the moment to tell him Maggie had always found her presence an insult and an injury. Sometimes a cold war was very hard to detect. Her face had paled with a whole power of beauty. It was obvious she was struggling with some kind of emotion. She lifted her head, braced for effort, and he gave a short laugh.

'Poor old Kat! Hard to capture and harder to hold. It's time you learnt to live comfortably with what you are, and what you've got.'

'I didn't make myself!' she said a little wildly.

'Neither you did. The heart, the brain, the nervous system were all there before you were born – to a degree, out of your control. But the old childhood trauma just isn't valid any more, my lamb. You've proved over and over that you've got what it takes to be a success anywhere. You can't want it all. Life's object isn't happiness, jewel-flower. It's learning, experience, a full life. I just thought I'd mention it so you'd give up this search for the impossible. You don't have to tell me Maggie is your big stumbling block, but you've built her up in your imagination, which you have to admit is colourful enough. She does tend to tell people what they don't care to hear at precisely the moment they least care to hear it, but she's not all that bad – just an outstandingly poor diplomat!'

She flashed him a look he would not soon forget, the mute resigned sadness, then the haughty, burning melancholia and resentment. 'God, you're like a nightingale shut up in a cage,' he muttered with the faintest, dangerous violence.

'And you've always demanded my twittering, blind obedience!' In the sudden gloom of the hangar, her skin gleamed opalescent. She swallowed a little, his eyes still hard on her, as if she was sitting beside not a man but a tiger.

'You're not going to take cover, this time, Kat!' he warned her. 'As elusive as ever. This time I'm going to jolt you wide awake. You're young and you're gifted, and if you weren't conceited enough already, I'd say you were truly beautiful with that element of strangeness true beauty demands. You've no reason at all to be sad and afraid of tomorrow – and there's not a bit of use looking at me as though I'm a thousand enemies rolled into one. I'm Big Brother Thorn, remember?'

She leaned over suddenly and nipped at his hand, her startlingly blue eyes faintly malicious. 'I have a view of your character that's entirely my own. You're gold, Thorn McCabe. Pure gold!'

'My angel!' His black eyes narrowed over her with languid grace. 'Let's say I understood you long before you ever saw yourself. It's given me a priceless advantage, so save the frosty, complicated glances. Your wild little ways always caught my attention!'

Katia wanted to say something, but found herself unable to speak. Instead she looked faintly shocked, traitorous little waves of fierce loyalty and resentment mingling and washing unchecked over her face. Then and for a long time she was completely unaware of the weapon nature had given her, the ability to arouse a man's deepest feelings. Her blue eyes slightly misted and she looked back at Thorn with a quality to her face that drove him suddenly towards violence. He twisted half up in the small cockpit to shield her with his lean, taut body, caught the point of her chin and dropped a brief, hard kiss on her parted mouth.

'Welcome home, jewel-flower. The moment of truth can't be put off any longer!'

Heat swept through her blood like a fever, driving so deep that her heart gave a great lunge, then quivered in shock. She felt stripped to the skin, exposed to the west wind that swept everything before it. But he had moved on and she followed, her face brushed with a terrible comprehension, unable to check her trembling as she dropped into his outstretched arms.

Oh, Thorn! Instinctively she touched her breast, such was the pain. Then the children were there, hugging her with reciprocal delight, Susan more restrained in her bright pleasure, both of them exclaiming over her clothes and her appearance, demanding to know, almost on cue, what she had brought them, for she never failed to arrive with something to delight them. What staff there were working in the vicinity seemed to crowd into the hangar, and Katia, like the accomplished actress she was, went through all the graceful little motions of reunion, hearing from all of them the best news of all, that Miz McCabe was improving. Moving out into the light, his bare head tilted back so that the sun gleamed on his face, was Thorn.

Her soul flew to him, while her body remained behind, her arms twined lovingly around the slight waists of her two little stepsisters, symbols of their strange relationship, intricate fold upon fold. What had lain dormant for so long was now revealed to her,

71

the first break in the wall with which she had surrounded herself – a keen punishment and one she could not escape.

She contemplated the two glowing chrysanthemum faces upturned to her and saw the visible imprint of McCabe. Physically and temperamentally they bore little resemblance to her, yet the blood ties ran deep. Gently she touched her lips to each forehead in turn, smiling before the waves of love that reached her, a talisman she could wear against Maggie and Carunya. She was an old woman now of twenty-two, no longer an over-emotional child, with Big Brother Thorn to fill the emptiness of her heart and teach her sensible conduct.

He stood by the big, powerful station wagon, one with his background, watching their approach. The children, radiant, blonde and kissed by the sun. Katia, whitely remote as a magnolia, moving delicately on her long, spirited legs. Something in his gleaming dark eyes plunged deep into her heart. For an instant she looked like the little wild one his father had dubbed her, a small creature in extreme peril, then she had settled herself gracefully in the front seat of the station wagon while the children spilled into the back seat, hanging over the seat, chattering happily with not even the rudiments of restraint.

Only once on the trip back to the Big House did Katia allow her eyes to rest on the handsome, arrogant profile cast out of bronze. The black eyes lightly touched her and through her blood ran a wild, sad longing. Yet nothing was happening. Thorn was only looking at her. She returned his gaze with a reaction she could not control, or indeed seemed aware of, an innocent and youthful sensuality and an immeasurable loneliness. Carunya had always been hostile to her, and Thorn *was* Carunya, passionately devoted to the land. To love Thorn, the man, not her childhood's champion, was to form an alliance with chaos. Already a driving, bitter-sweet excitement was causing her to lose her bearings.

In the sultry heat the lagoon flashed by, a place of green shadows and rustlings and silvery tranquillity, the calming influence of trees, leaves and water, the wind-stirred flower dances. Katia could still feel its spell. Trees were real people; the ghost gums, the paperbarks, the tall coolibahs and blossoming bauhinias, alive with the opal and flame-tinted birds, humming with the soft, curious singing of the aboriginal women as they collected wild honey.

In her ear Debby was declaring the new hairstyle was 'positively romantic' and she must have 'hundreds of admirers', right at the age to be fascinated by her smooth and beautiful stepsister. Katia smiled a light, 'Not at all, darling!' and studiously avoided a slanting black glance, keeping her eyes on the track. It levelled away to an avenue of shrubs all heavily in blossom and scent, bowing their heads to the sun. Up ahead, beyond the bend, one could first glimpse the house and be caught up in the past, the serene, mellowed beauty of stone walls and iron lace. Her mother had worked miracles with the grounds, the hundreds and hundreds of plantings, the beautiful bursts of ornamental grasses and ferns, the latticed redwood gazebo Katia had sought sanctuary in as a child, lying full length on the built-in benches.

At the thought of her mother, as at any time in the

preceding hours, Katia's eyes misted over. Her mind filled with images and her heart hammered on her ribs. She could see a pretty, fair face with hair in a burnished halo around a neat, well-shaped head. A pearl-shaped tear slid down her cheek and Debby leaned over and brushed it from her chin.

'Mummy's all right!' she whispered emphatically. 'She's our spunky girl!'

'A girl in a million,' Thorn said quietly, without turning his head. 'You won't find her much altered, Kat, for all the nice, rounded contours have faded away a little. But now *you're* home. Say it, Kat. *Home!*'

'You make it sound like a present I can give you!' she said, wondering for a moment at the depth to his voice, intensified.

'That's perfectly true! I think I'm entitled to one after all this time.'

His smile, faintly sardonic, puzzled her too. 'But I've given you tons of things,' she protested. 'Your birthday present cost me the earth.'

'And didn't I sing praises over it?' he inquired with a tantalizing inflection in his vibrant voice. 'As I recall, I exhausted the matter with magnanimous thanks. That's not what I'm talking about, Kat, as well you know.'

She shook her glossy black head, a shadow over her features. 'You've tormented me ever since I can remember!'

His lean powerful hands gripped the wheel. Hands that could grasp reality hard. '*And* I still cling to my habits. You shouldn't let me treat you so badly, Kat. Tell me, what is it about me you most dislike?'

74

'Your arrogance could suffer a few blows,' she suggested lightly enough, but Debby, the ever-interested listener, broke in with extreme acuteness:

'Oh, don't be silly, Thorn. She *loves* you, don't you, Katy darling?' Beside her, Susan's blue eyes radiated a matching, smiling sincerity. Oh yes, Katy loved Thorn. There had never been any doubt about that.

'Don't try to work it out!' Thorn warned in a soft drawl. 'You'll go out of your mind. The sweet, terrible game of love!'

She felt a little shiver of fear, but her spirit answered for her. 'I don't go out of my mind so easily, Thorn McCabe!'

'There's a marvellous reply to that, but I won't tell you at the moment.' Thorn gazed into her eyes with a mocking, tranquil smile and Debby burst in, gaily intelligent:

'Well, if you didn't go out of your mind, you could go grey. You'd look terribly handsome with grey hair, Thorn!'

'Sit back, Debby, like a good girl. Your tongue never fails you in any situation. Sue, wind the window up a bit, there's too much dust getting into the car.' He glanced sideways at Katia, her delicate face as remote as a dreaming figure. 'Don't worry, little one, it will all turn out well.'

She wouldn't, couldn't look at him, for an abyss had opened up, leaving her as shallow and transparent as a rock pool. 'Don't be so nice to me!' she said with a graceful, disciplined movement of her hand over her hair.

'Sometimes I can't help it!'

The sun laid a glimmer of gold over his dark skin,

and she knew without looking the exact angle of his head, the clear cut of his mouth and chin. 'We've been through so much together, I suppose we're nearly tied to one another,' she said with a swift and charming abandon, and heard his dark-shaded laugh.

'I've never been so sweetly insulted in my life! Now why do you say such things to me, Katia Grenville?' His eyes rested on the pale, pure contours of what would be indestructible beauty. He himself came of stock hard as steel, but the McCabes had never produced a stunning young creature like Katia with her laughter and tears and undeniable gifts. 'A long pause ensues. All right, we'll discuss it when you're your old self again!'

She turned to smile at him, her equanimity restored. 'A thousand delicate apologies, but I'm not about to undergo any psychoanalyst's session. Nor even for you, McCabe, will I reveal my innermost self!' The anxious premonitions about her mother that had weighed on her so heavily seemed to be abating. Her eyes, intensely blue, deeply feminine in their thick black webbing of lashes, clung to his face with an allure fairly or unfairly handed out in the cradle.

'Don't use your famous talents on me,' he cautioned her. 'We all know you're a star!'

'But isn't it marvellous to have a famous relative?' Debby demanded of him, butting in. 'You can't imagine, Kat, how proud we are. All of our friends are green with envy now you've made the big time, and you're so terribly chic, even in slacks, and *dreamy* at the same time. I can never manage to look like that!'

'Do you try?' Sue inquired with gentle malice.

'That's what I like about you!' Debby said in a

quick, unbroken aside to her sister, no rift between them ever irreconcilable. 'How do you do it, Kat?' she persisted, looking at Katia's shiny dark head.

'I really don't know, pet!' Katia rested her head back against the seat, from the tone of her voice not even considering.

'Seriously, don't you ever look in your mirror?' Sue inquired, meaning it. Of late, she did a great deal of it herself.

Katia roused herself to turn and look into the two familiar fair faces. 'But you're beautiful, Sue. Debby too, both of you!' She spoke with absolute conviction so that Debby crowed, nearly flinging herself over the seat:

'Maybe we are, but look at *you*!'

Instantly Thorn turned on her. 'Debby, Debby, where's all the ladylike grace your mother insists upon? A little more of that might make you more beautiful, not to mention that a true lady always keeps her mouth shut!'

Debby sat back and crossed her legs under her. 'You ought to be boiled in coconut oil for that!'

Thorn regarded her thoughtfully in the rear vision mirror. 'I'll remember. I have a wonderful memory!'

'Don't you ever!' Debby retorted, rattling on. He smiled at her infectious good humour and she blew him a flourishing kiss. It was quite impossible to be angry with her ever. The pebbled drive broke out into a wide sweep and there ahead was the house, very sure of itself. It stood in its beautiful setting, an added enhancement, if indeed it needed it.

'We're home again!' Sue said happily, her soft,

golden-brown brows level. 'And tea in Mummy's room!'

Katia, her eyes veiled and mysterious, was lost in her memories. Thorn flung her a brilliant black glance. 'Life's pretty painful at times, isn't it? But a lot depends on ourselves. Rough seas, smooth seas, the odd cyclone or two. The thing is to keep sailing through it!'

'S'truth, love, we haven't all got your high purpose!' Debby broke in with a touch of brilliant insight and the oddest notion that she had to protect her beloved stepsister.

Thorn merely propelled his lean, long torso forward a little and pulled over off the drive. 'Debby, you adorable child, my patience has just run out. Get out!' he said in a strong, positive voice.

'Orders from the Big Boss to the Little Boss!' Debby said, surrendering to his unassailable authority. She put her hand on the door catch and Thorn gave his attractive laugh, relenting:

'Such instant obedience is a pleasure to see! For that, you can get in again!'

'I'm indispensable here, that's why. Katy's no gloom addict, not the way *she* laughs!'

'Why, thank you, darling, I love you for that!'

'Ditto!' Debby said, and leaned forward and kissed her stepsister's satiny cheek in a moment of mutual tenderness.

'You love playing games, don't you?' Katia demanded, looking at Thorn's vivid, autocratic face.

'More often than not!'

He didn't look at her but she could *feel* his brilliant gaze, her senses seemed to have become so heightened. Irresistibly her eyes were drawn to his mouth, against her own inclinations. The imprint of it on her own would remain with her more vividly than any other experience. She would never let go of it. Not for hundreds of years. And with this realization she arrived at the crossroads in her young life where only Thorn seemed the true road with Maggie to mock her stumbling steps.

Spearheads of pampas grass stood motionless above the flowers that spread at their feet and the warm, dry, smell of the land was part of the consciousness of the moment and forever to be remembered. How else could she explain that sense of being committed to Carunya beyond any possible withdrawal, try as she might. There was no way of wiping out the past. There *was* no past. Only yesterday, or last year, she thought, or when I was ten or twenty. Carunya was a dream from which she would never wake.

Thorn, glancing sideways at her expressive young face, was moved to compassion. The time was not yet before Katia would be free of all her complications and find the deep sense of harmony her nature craved.

'How many miles to Babylon?' he asked, seemingly idly, to no one in particular, and Debby, highly diverted, craned forward to look into his face.

'What would you be blithering about, you poor man? Is it some kind of riddle?'

'Only Kat knows the answer to that!' His slanting black gaze touched the pulse in her throat, his dark face full of vitality and power.

'Oh, in that case, she'll tell me later!' Debby announced with a complacent look on her face, for once insensitive to undercurrents. Susan, two years older, on the threshold of young womanhood, had a far more perceptive awareness. Katia, who could laugh and sing and act out stories and ride like the wind! Katia, whom she had loved for as far back as she could remember, was different from all of them. She could recognize this fact once and for all and store it away in her mind.

Katia, so devastatingly charming, with her black hair and her blue eyes and her white, white skin. The lost, dreaming expression that contrasted so vividly with the random bouts of temperament when she blew up a storm, full of poetry and wild beauty; a sadness and excitement and vivacity that broke like sea foam over all of them, such was her fascination.

Katia was her half-sister, but to Thorn she was no relation at all, and what else Susan thought, she told no one at all.

From the high, handsome window of an upstairs bedroom Miss Maggie McCabe looked down at the courtyard, veiled thinly by the long lacy curtains. It was not her habit to spy in a corner, but something she had never put a name to held her there. She stood perfectly still with a set white face and unshifting blue gaze, a handsome, ageing woman, tall, rather heavily built, her once luxuriant gold hair rolled into a heavy, colourless knot.

She might have been a statue, cold and indifferent, but indifference did not live in her then, for the eyes betrayed a capacity for jealousy and hostility that had the stuff of drama. A clear young voice, controlled and lovely, floated up to her ears and just for a moment a hectic pink showed on the statue's prominent cheekbones.

So she was back! Even at a distance Maggie felt the same sense of affront at those improbable good looks, the 'gardenia' quality that had no place in the sun and the golden heat. The raven-haired creature with her foibles and demands and clinging devotion to Thorn. Maggie McCabe had no use for her, never had. An outsider was an outsider and no amount of tiresome talk or family good will would bridge the gulf.

Suddenly Maggie sensed a shadow in the doorway and turned fully towards it. She said nothing, but subjected her visitor to a merciless scrutiny, a slight working of the lips, and a cold flash in the eyes that kept Sarah Walker, for all her calm competence and good sense, rooted to the spot, unable to move or speak.

'Well, don't stand there gaping! What is it?' The voice came hard and forced and it stirred Sarah to full life, the long years of coping with difficult patients allowing her to keep her voice courteous and pleasant in the face of such cold and repelling arrogance.

'I beg your pardon, Miss McCabe. I'm sorry I startled you. Mr. McCabe has arrived home with Miss Katia.'

'So I see!' the tall figure said with an effort, and fell silent, leaving Sarah with the oddest notion that it was her dismal lot to be the bearer of ill tidings.

The woman was uncanny with her heavy chignon and her cold eyes, the mouth firmly shut, the nostrils now quivering like leaves in the storm. She was, Sarah considered, not for the first time, without a particle of personal charm, but the decided knack for making Sarah feel an intrusive, uninvited guest in an otherwise happy home. Sarah hesitated for a moment, simply at a loss, when Miss McCabe spoke.

'If you came to ask me to the tea party in my sister-in-law's room,' she said brusquely, 'I must decline with thanks. Despite your professional assurances, I consider it highly inadvisable, for reasons one would have thought would be obvious!'

At the heavily implied criticism, Sarah flushed to the collar of her uniform, almost jolted into speaking her mind, her sense of injustice fully aroused. Caution, born of wisdom, made her let a few seconds slip by to sober her. She felt extreme distaste for this coldly fierce woman facing her, this left-over relic of a despotic past, so that in spite of the heat she felt chilled. Looking straight into the pale, heavy-lidded eyes, she managed mildly enough:

'Mrs. McCabe is showing wonderful progress. We shall all take the greatest care not to over-excite her. It's a cup of tea, after all, with her loved ones, not a party!'

The older woman rejected this explanation with a grim smile. 'Would you be kind enough to leave now? I might take this opportunity to inform you that this side of the house is out of bounds to you in your business. Your position here is by no means social, and I fail to see why you should look so unpleasantly surprised. My sister-in-law is far too soft-hearted, but that is her affair. Should her condition deteriorate, of course, that will be another matter. What *I* have told you is final. Good day.'

Sarah whirled about, her heart thumping with savage dislike. Whatever else one thought of Maggie McCabe, she had a supernatural gift for upsetting people. It was quite possible before she left, she would be required to turn out her bags in case she had made

82

off with the silver. 'A frightful old dame!' Sarah found herself muttering, striving to impose calm on her agitated nerves.

Once or twice she had heard the odd rumour that Miss Katia and Miss McCabe were not on the best of terms. If so, Sarah could understand why. Maggie McCabe was a dragon with those she considered of the lesser orders. To a sensitive child, not in the fullest sense 'one of the family', she just could have been a disaster or the essence of conflict. Whatever it was, Sarah had the certain feeling that the coming of Katia Grenville to Carunya had ostensibly changed everything. The frightful inner rigidity of the woman! She found herself reliving those brief moments when only a slight brush had shown it up.

With a great sense of relief Sarah hurried down the corridor and crossed to the west wing, back to her charming and courageous patient, her pretty hair brushed like an aureole around her fined-down face, her expressive eyes filled with anticipatory pleasure. Carole McCabe, a miracle of womanliness, after her sister-in-law.

CHAPTER FIVE

EARLY next morning Katia padded down the corridor to her mother's room, clad in a loose lemon-yellow silk robe, her black hair cascading back from her face. It was a beautiful morning, shimmering with light and swarms of birds. No early morning sounds of activity reached this part of the house, so mellow and steeped in traditional beauty, and suddenly it came to Katia that despite all the old conflicts, some part of her loved the house, welcomed it over and over; the large, high-ceilinged rooms that flowed one into the other with nothing to mar their serenity, beautiful by any standards.

The ivory and almond green moulded door to her mother's room lay open and Katia paused on the threshold, aware of the little feminine touches introduced since Charles had died. Propped up on her pillows, the sun settling round her shoulders like some beautiful bedjacket, was her mother, an aureole blur before Katia's suddenly glistening eyes. She blinked quickly, bringing everything into closer focus, love filling her face and shining out of her eyes.

'Good morning, Mamma!'

The magic welcome! Carole felt a flood of warmth and her heart moved in her with a gentle, healing purr. 'It is, darling. It really is!'

She lifted her hand, and Katia closed the space between them, pressing herself mutely to her mother's heart, relieved beyond words, wondering how they

84

were ever going to survive being apart again. Above her dark head Carole's eyes gleamed softly with a light that came from the soul and went a long way towards restoring her body. She was the eternal mother, reversing the positions, offering to her child a limitless capacity for tenderness and comfort. Stroking her daughter's night-dark head, she was reminded again of Shawn. He could never truly be absent, for one could never be unmindful that Katia was her father's daughter, though occasionally Carole fancied she caught an expression of her own, but that was all.

Sarah, entering the room noiselessly with a breakfast tray, was the most enchanted of observers. It pleased and reassured her greatly to see the magical transformation in her patient. Miss Katia was the answer they had all been looking for, with the possible exception of the Big Old Missy, as Minnie dubbed her, but Sarah quickly dismissed all thought of Miss Maggie McCabe from such a charming, heartwarming scene. A horribly unsympathetic sort of woman, Sarah thought from the depths of a very alien nature.

She could still feel the shock of the girl's beauty. It was startling really, for even though she had seen all the children's photographs of their stepsister, Sarah had been unprepared for the colouring. It was like being confronted with an endless vista of blossom, all the springs and the summers come together, for Sarah, though devoid of beauty herself in its physical manifestations, was wonderfully admiring and generous to it in others. She glanced again at the girl. No make-up. A clean morning face, no pins in her thick fall of hair, bare feet, a beautiful sunshine-coloured robe like a cocoon around her slight frame.

Youth and beauty! Sarah thought; it's terrifying and rather sad too. This girl had a curious, vulnerable, sensitive look as though life would never be easy for her, and none of her mother's sensible earth-bound quality. Both faces had turned to smile at her, presenting the greatest possible contrast in type and colouring, but just for an instant Sarah imagined she caught an identical expression. A loving heart! That was it, Sarah thought. They had it, both of them.

'Good morning!' she smiled. 'I didn't know you'd be here, Miss Katia, but I think I've brought you plenty. What would you like, tea or coffee?'

'Coffee if you have it,' the inimitable voice said. 'That would be lovely!'

'Coffee it is!' Sarah promised, and turned her attentions to her patient. 'Words are superfluous, but I'll say them all the same. You look marvellous this morning, Mrs. McCabe!'

'Thank you, Sarah. I feel it!' her patient smiled, the sunlight sheening the tips of her curly hair to small flames. Katia regarded her mother silently and saw that this was indeed so. Happily she patted the small fine-boned hand resting lightly in her own and moved off the bed allowing Sarah to adjust the breakfast tray across her mother's knees with her usual efficiency.

Katia moved backwards towards the window. The view from her mother's room was the best of all. Breath-takingly lovely, the lagoon bathed in the soft, translucent light of morning. The air was coming in soft, scented wafts and she felt the young blood rise in her. Later on she would take Jamba out. Princess of the stud. Perfection on four legs, Thorn called her, all shining muscles and delicate, incredible beauty with

86

nothing to flaw her, strength as well as elegance from a long line of superb breeding. Laughingly Thorn claimed that Jamba went lame every time anyone else but Katia or young Micky, the little aboriginal attendant, tried to ride her. Jamba was temperamental, but Katia knew the filly trusted her.

Gracefully she came to rest in an armchair, shoulders sloping forward, head tilted back, her hands cupping the white porcelain coffee cup Sarah passed to her like some medieval chalice while Sarah in turn watched discreetly, fascinated by the girl's every little movement as though she had never seen a woman eat or drink in her life before, she later thought humorously. Gradually the conversation settled into a small silence, that was, and all three were gratefully aware of it, the silence of great contentment.

It was thrilling, absolutely thrilling. Katia felt drunk with it – the same satisfaction and excitement she felt after an especially good performance. That wonderful glow of achievement that left no room for the small niggling doubts and discontents.

Out in the grasslands the silence was a rare thing, a still green world before man ever set foot in it, and all around them the wild magnificence of the hill country, the burning, shifting sands, the rolling red lines of the sandhills, strange bizarre bastions from immemorial times, attended by the silver-blue waves of mirage. It was a harsh, haunting landscape, unique in all the world. Only the house stood alone in its little green lake of civilization, for almost on its doorstep was the land, with all its wild untamed grandeur, casting a giant shadow over all of them.

Carunya, she thought, looking right into the eye of the sun. Carunya with its wealth and griefs and nameless graves, stark relics of the short, terrible wars waged between black man and white. But she wouldn't think of that – *couldn't*, with Jamba, the filly of great quality, obeying the slightest indication of hand or heel, moving so sweetly beneath her. The long stretch of thick, springy grass slipped by under them with only the soft drumming of hooves to make music in her ears. The warm, spicy air parted around horse and rider, lifting Katia's hair from her nape and her ears.

'My beauty!' Katia breathed over the satiny neck, and Jamba, not one brown hair in her jet black coat, pricked her ears with the air of a princess receiving her due. Nearing the meandering green line of the river Katia pulled the filly up into a slow canter, closed her knees and headed towards the long line of bushes. With an incredibly smooth action Jamba rose into the air, soaring like a blackbird, landing smoothly and neatly on the far side. It was rapturous, their flight, and a rare exhilaration; a far cry from the often frenetic world of the theatre.

Later she lay on her back in the green turf, watching a single wisp of cloud sail past in the peacock-blue sky. A short distance away from her, Jamba, white blaze on her forehead, was cropping over the sweet grass in her dainty, superior fashion, the bit making small sounds in the crystal-clear silence. With a faint, blissful sigh, she closed her eyes, all her senses alive, responding to the fragrant scent of the cane grass, the shivery beautiful sound of the wind in the leaves.

Pulses quickened within her body, for the spirit of the bush was upon her while she lay like a small wild

88

creature, frozen behind a feathery screen of leaves. The clear, limpid notes of the butcher bird held aloft for a moment, then filtered to the ground, the signal to flight for hundreds of tiny shell parrots and chats, the sun glinting off feathers and wings, jewel flashes of crimson and yellow and green. The land had been blessed with rain and it smelled sweet, the sap rising in the trees, the bauhinias, the limewoods, the white-boled eucalyptus, the homes of the kingfishers, the rainbow birds and the busy, honey-making bees. Along the shadowy, golden green banks of the river tiny white and gold wild flowers rode the tall waves of grass and down further in the dense glade, wild orchids and fringed trunga lilies grew in great clumps.

It was no wonder at all that Thorn felt such a great love for this land of his. The need to have and to hold for it possessed the capacity to stir all the great emotions of the human heart. The land could, if you listened, talk to you, tell you its moods and its secrets, and if you were initiated, its spirit links. The land was immense, old as time, worn to strange patterns by the all-powerful sun and the winds, but it had great authority, a tangible spirit that hovered over the place. If Katia would only allow herself the truth it had entered her when she had been a child.

A thick silver spider web strung across the topmost branches of the spindly acacia behind her suddenly shook in the air. She heard nothing, but a shiver ran the full length of her spine, a reaction to strong male vibrations. She gave a little muffled cry and half sprang up, shocked to find herself almost in Thorn's arms, without defence against the stir and the challenge in him, the very male life force.

I do love you, she thought, in a kind of shocked fright. Truly, truly love you. The magic of Thorn. She had always needed it and somehow she had always known. Thorn, the one who was different, and even as a child she had the wisdom to know it.

There were traces of a question on his dark face, his mouth faintly indulgent, a depth of mockery in his dark, slanting eyes. 'Don't look so guilty, Kat! What on earth were you doing?' The timbre of his voice, so amused and sardonic, was a shot of adrenalin that helped fight the battle for her.

'Weaving fantasies, perhaps!' she said lightly. She was looking directly into his eyes, the sunlight between them, but her faint little smile never quite made it. Something about his expression made her tilt her face defiantly, the dark hair and alabaster skin, the flower blue eyes.

He put out a hand and pushed the black cloud of her hair back from her face, leaving her skin and her small ear exposed.

'The right bones, the right hollows and curves, beautiful skin! Some women I've known use their beauty like a whip, yet you seem unaware of it. Just imagine, Kat!'

The touch of his hand was making the music start as it never had before and she put up her own hand almost defensively.

'What's this,' he asked in an amused, level voice, 'an injured bird's wing?'

She could feel the fire rise in her cheeks and her hair became a dark stormy cloud about her small face. Her heart was beating rather wildly with inner anxiety as if she had walked unknowingly into the tiger's cage.

Thorn was high-tension dynamism, a kind of magnetic power as if he had the whole world and her too in the palm of his hand. His hand slid under her chin and forced her head up. 'A blue butterfly, pinned, but still fluttering! Relax, Kat, you won't die of it!' With a faint masculine impatience he pushed her back into the fresh, prickly softness of the cane grass.

'One day I'm going to go away and shut the door forever on Carunya!' she said with a suggestion of temperament.

'It's all right, Kat,' he said, an ironical little catch of laughter in his voice. 'I'll get right there between you and it. Besides, it's ridiculous to be violent about the past.' He dropped back on the grass beside her and she shut her eyes against his whole outline, the incredibly, intoxicatingly, familiar strangeness of it all.

'You're the real viper in my bosom,' she said theatrically, and he burst out laughing, tweaking a silky strand of her hair.

'Why are you so damned sure?'

'I just am.'

'You really don't tell the truth, Kat!' he said from somewhere above her,

'*Your* truth, you mean. We all have different ones.'

'Well, you're in the best place to find out!' Without warning his hand slid under her hair and pinned the nape of her neck. 'You know, Kat, I've never put you over my knee. It's a terrible omission in my life.'

Her eyes flew open and drowned in his own. 'Well, it's too late now. One can't move backwards through time.'

'By the same token, there are some things none of us

can prevent – and spare me the devouring feminine glances. One of these days you're going to carry me down into the water if I'm not careful!'

She drew a long, quivering breath. 'Honestly, Thorn, sometimes you wear a cloud around you that makes conversation impossible!'

'Come on, baby. Leave it!'

'Just as you say, Thorn.' Tension and excitement had slipped into her face.

'I've always liked you to have as much peace of mind as possible. No inner conflicts.'

'How do you know I have them?' she queried, her whole body taking on a new animation.

'Oh, baby!' He touched a lean finger to her cheek and her skin tightened electrically. 'I've told you before, Kat, I'm very clever at deciphering the expressions on your face.'

'Don't I know it! You make me feel the most blatant of scripts.'

'How's Ivor?' he asked, taking her right off guard.

'A very civilized man!' she said severely.

'An unrelenting gentleman, or a demanding lover?'

'Excuse me, Thorn McCabe,' she said, swinging up, graceful and electric in her movements. He looked across at her, black eyes narrowing.

'Well?'

She jerked away a little wildly, but he held her still, the best and the worst kind of man, with the power to make a woman feel just that – a woman.

'You don't strike me as a girl who's heard the cymbals clang and the drums go bang! And don't act as if you're about to flee. It's so long since we had a nice old-fashioned chat.'

'Ivor and I console each other!' she said sweetly, then winced a little at the sudden pain in her hand. Thorn released it slowly.

'What is it the Chinese say, marriages are made in the moon?'

'So that's why so many husbands take flight,' she said, mock-flippant, feeling as though she was really being pushed to the edge of a cliff.

'Has Ivor said he loves you?'

'Yes,' she said briefly, struck by the sudden grimness that touched his voice. 'Have you ever been in love, Thorn?'

'No good, jewel-flower!'

'It was worth a try. I must confess I thought so once or twice. Remember Marcia Noble?'

'No.' He lay back in the grass and twisted his hands under his head, looking beyond her to the sky.

'Really?' she asked, trying not to look at him. 'I suffer from a very good memory myself. An occupational disease, I suppose.'

'In that case, you'll remember we were talking about Ivor. Invite him out.'

'Just like that. I'm terribly beholden to you, Thorn McCabe.'

'Quaint word! Is that the actress in you?'

'I love the theatre!' she said, despite herself her eyes straying to him, all her resolutions going up in smoke at the sight of him.

'This environment suits you equally well.' He turned his head abruptly, his eyes slipping over her.

'Luverly. You don't mean that, why don't you say it?'

'I don't mean that!' he repeated humorously. 'Actually, **Kat**, I do. Unlike you, my lamb, I've no inclination to act!'

She looked at him for a moment with troubled sapphire eyes, and his hard, handsome face softened.

'There's something haunting about you, little one, Something vulnerable. How am I ever going to be able to toughen you up?'

'I've never taken advantage of the affection you feel for me, have I, Thorn?'

He brought her down in the grass beside him with dispassionate violence. 'Why say that to me?'

'Forget it, darling, I'm the happiest girl in the world!' She laughed a little; only after she had said it did she tremble at how easily the endearment had slipped out. She lay back on the jade green carpet staring forlornly into his face, the brilliant black gaze that was so utterly fathomless. *Fathomless*. Often as happened with her, a fragment of verse slipped into her mind and she said it out loud, a soft, woman chant:

'Deep into that darkness peering, long I stood there wondering, fearing, doubting, dreaming dreams no mortal ever dreamed before.'

He pressed her back into the ground with careless strength. 'No need to tell me that's out of a poem. Poe, isn't it?'

'Yes. I'd forgotten for a moment how well read you are.' He made not the slightest attempt to release her and she found herself almost pleading: 'Please, Thorn!' She was breathing quickly, her slight breast rising and falling as though there was a quarrel between them.

Taut pressure lines seemed to form around his

mouth. 'It would be easier for you, Kat, to roll a stone up a mountain than escape your destiny. I think you love your Ivor a little, but you lack the faculty to settle down happily with second best.'

'I do love him!' she said with a strange blaze in her remarkable eyes.

'You don't!' His dark face was hard and derisive. 'Though when you give a little love and take it, it's always there, somewhere, an echo and a memory. Even if it gets buried for whole years at a time and has to be dredged up some three o'clock in the morning.' He looked down at her flower face, the passionate nature she was scarcely hiding. 'Has he stayed at your apartment?'

'Of course not!' Strange blue lights leapt in her eyes.

'A lover without indiscretion is no lover at all!' he said lightly, with a careless flick of his power.

'A stirring announcement! You're a conceited devil, McCabe. I remember all the wild oats you've sown, even if you don't.'

Thorn suddenly laughed, a cynical sparkle in his brilliant dark eyes. 'Don't talk, Kat. We're so seldom alone these days.'

'You don't need me or anyone,' she said softly. 'You're a self-generating person. There aren't too many of them about!'

He lay back, indolent grace in every line of him. 'You've certainly got me type-cast. A real tough guy!'

'Aren't you?'

'Ask all the leading questions you like! Of course I am. I've got to be or I wouldn't last a day in my line, but I still don't go around gobbling up baby lambs.'.

'No,' she said with a familiar rush of contrition, avoiding his intent dark eyes. 'I suppose it's the power of personality. Every day made up of danger and decisions, taking risks. It's part of your natural background and it makes you quite different. You're not, for instance, the type of man to be dominated by a woman, or even, I think, gently led. A lot of men are. Some of my distinguished colleagues in the theatre are quite terrified of their wives and womenfolk. Clever, experienced men turn into anxious schoolboys about getting home on time.' She turned and studied his amused expression. 'I can't imagine you in any circumstances taking that!'

'I should hope not!' He moved unexpectedly and enclosed her wrist. 'Not even you, lorelei, could get away with that!'

No, she thought plaintively, and tried unsuccessfully to free her wrist. Thorn would demand a woman's deepest submission and he would get it. Though he was firm to the point of plenty of control, he could be wondrously gentle too, as he was with his horses. Never, never ruthless handling. Thorn and his horses! They were inseparable, and thinking this, Katia smiled, an unconscious rising provocation in the curve of her mouth, the angle of her slight feminine body. The warm fresh grass, the wild flowers, the crushed mosses breathed into the quiet, spicy air.

'Comfortable?' she asked him.

'Acutely so. A charming little idyll!' His slanting black gaze studied her with clinical thoroughness. 'You're extravagantly beautiful, Kat. When you're away, it's a matter of some anxiety to me if you'll come to any harm. You might warn all those clever, experienced men about me, then they'll know what to expect.'

'I can look after myself!' she volunteered, letting the warm air play over her nape.

'Oddly enough, I believe you can.'

Her fingers quivered in his and he let them go. 'Carole is so much better this morning,' he said with some satisfaction. 'A return to her old self. You've been for her like a shower of rain in the desert – little short of miraculous!'

She looked down at him quickly, her voice silky soft. 'I wondered how you knew which way I came. You've got Mother wrapped around your little finger.'

'We're like that!' He lightly crossed two fingers, his eyes glinting, but Katia was deadly serious, her sapphire eyes shimmering.

'I'm very grateful for it, Thorn. A hundred years from now I'll remember how kind you've been to us both. Those early days!'

He reached out, his lean hands closing in at her waist. 'You silly child, what are you on about now? Carole was my father's wife, his widow. Quite apart from the fact that it's absurdly easy to love her for herself. Now you, spirit-child, are an entirely different proposition – a real cross, but I can bear it. Tell, me how did you manage to elude the kids? They were rarin' to go!'

His hands had left her, but she still felt the tingling warmth of them. 'I just told them I'd like to ride out by myself for a while. They're old enough now to accept that. In fact, they're maturing very well. I'm very proud of them. So golden with such playful grace. It's

97

the strangest thing, Thorn, but lately I have this awful sensation of being cramped. Trapped if you like!'

'Would it have anything to do with Ivor?' he asked in a voice that sent a faint shiver through her. 'He must have asked you to marry him. I can imagine how you'd react to that. You're rather unusual in that regard!'

Katia's smile held a twist of belief. She knew she wasn't easily attracted to men. In fact she was extremely fastidious. Not for her the easy experiments, assessing, testing every man she met. It wasn't her nature. If she could bear to examine the heart of the matter she had only ever been attracted to one man, Thorn, and he had never been hers to keep. Ivor was something else again, a defence and a hiding place, though even that had become untenable.

'Love's not a game,' she said sadly, 'or if it is most adults expect to play it to the conclusion. I don't want that. I think Ivor fears I'm a little cold!'

He muttered some violent exclamation. 'Hang that! All your instincts are right. Just see you stick to them. It looks very much to me that you'd better put Ivor out of his misery. It's not fair otherwise. Women like you, Kat, only occur once or twice in a man's lifetime. I'm beginning to feel sorry for him, and that will never do. Armstrong is due in this afternoon, we'll see what he has to say about your mother. I've discussed this with Sarah and I'm putting in a pool behind the house. The kids can keep going down to the lagoon if they like, but it will be too far for Carole. She's always loved the water. I'll get the boys started on it right away. She can get a little exercise that way with Sarah to supervise.' He paused for a moment and looked directly at Katia, the sun finding no flaw in her satiny young skin. 'What do you think of her?'

'Sarah? I like her very much. Her essential niceness shines through. I know she must have excellent qualifications, otherwise you wouldn't have hired her, and Mother likes her too. They're comfortable together and Sarah would never intrude. Mother so likes her privacy, and it's rather difficult.' She looked over at his strong dark face, anxieties and doubts pressing down on her. 'How am I ever going to leave Mother again?'

'That's for you to decide.' His darkly tanned face was inscrutable, closed up. No help there. 'Carole will come good again!' he promised her. 'Some things you feel in your bones. Next year the kids go to boarding school. Carole was saying before this that she might take a unit in the city to be near them and go back and forth. Naturally the children would come here in their holidays.'

'She never said anything to me.' Katia stared back at him.

'Well, it was never fully discussed. Could you give up your career, Kat? You've got what it takes, and there's a big, wide, wonderful world out there!'

Her pale, slender fingers tugged at a patch of grass. 'I'm not happy, Thorn.'

He made a sound of complete impatience, his chiselled mouth hardening. 'Don't talk *happy* to me, baby. Settle for a sense of purpose. Fulfilment if you like. Once the theatre was all you wanted, so you said, usually with floods of high-strung dramatics. If you loved this Ivor you'd be on cloud number seven, because that's the way you are!'

'I'll write to him and ask him out.' She closed her

eyes, a little drugged with the heat and his nearness. 'He's very busy, so he would only be able to stay for a few days. You'd like him, Thorn, he's a very interesting man.'

'So Carole said. Then it's settled. Ask him out and I'll give him the once-over. The very least I can do as Big Brother. Now get up,' he said, his breath sizzling her ear, his arms encircling her and drawing her to her feet. 'There might be snakes about.'

'Now's the time to tell me!' she said shakily, allowing herself the forbidden luxury of drawing on his radiant energy. Everything physical he did was so firm and decided, so stunning in its self-assurance, she had long since come to the conclusion that Thorn was confident as few men were confident.

'Why the little tremors?' he murmured. 'What is it that's so especially difficult you have to hide from it?'

Katia moved her shoulders in a little helpless shrug, doubting the wisdom of finding her voice. Thorn had a once-and-for-all advantage over her and now to be swept into a major foreign dimension.

'Little fool!' he said softly, and it was almost a caress. 'There's really a very simple solution, but I'm going to let you see it first. You can't opt out after all the time I've spent on you.'

The raw awareness of him stung her into speech, her voice holding an odd element of conflict. 'You think I'm a fugitive, don't you?'

His arm dropped to her shoulder and turned her around. 'Not at all, and stop all this madness. Courage is an integral part of your nature. You're like your mother in that way, born brave. It's this absurd sensitivity of yours that makes it so risky. Now come along, my contrary girl-child, and we'll take each day as it comes.' He stretched out his hand, his voice very calm, and after an instant's slight hesitation she took it. When had she ever been able to hold out against Thorn?

CHAPTER SIX

Miss Maggie McCabe did not greet. She waited to be greeted. She entered the living-room in her ancient but still elegant pure silk jersey evening gown, cleverly draped around her heavy but still handsome figure. She could have been a queen entering her kingdom. The house was her kingdom, in her own mind at least.

She proceeded to the quilted white and gold sofa with the eighteenth-century Chinese lacquered table in front of it, and seated herself with the greatest possible dignity and decorum. Never at any time of her life had she allowed herself the deplorable tendency to lounge or slouch and only on the day they brought in her beloved brother, Charles, did she come close to collapsing on to that same couch. It had been recovered since then, for she found she could not bear the sight of it.

From her manner one would have been forgiven in thinking her alone, but some short distance from her, Katia, in an exquisite blue chiffon gown, her eyes as brilliant as the gems at her ears and her throat, was arranging a cascade of wild orchids in the porcelain ginger jar. It was very original and effective and she had been very pleased with it until Maggie arrived and pronounced her invisible.

Deliberate. She does it deliberately, Katia thought, but made a mammoth effort to be polite.

'Good evening, Maggie. The children found these

this afternoon down by the lagoon. Beautiful, aren't they? You'd pay a fortune for them in the city. All ivory and almond and blush pink!' No answer seemed to be forthcoming, so she went on like a well rehearsed script. 'I thought we might have coffee afterwards around the Chinese table. It opens out. What do you think?'

'I've never cared to linger on and on after dinner,' Maggie offered in her repressive, well-bred voice, 'but as to that, you may have it where you like. I imagine you're an expert by now in the art of entertaining. I would hate anything to get spilled on it. As a family we treasure our things. Many of them are, as you know, extremely valuable!' She looked up all at once, fixing Katia with her pale, piercing scrutiny.

'Um, I know!' Katia murmured, finishing off her arrangement, feeling the old desire to fling a few of them at Maggie's head. 'I'm like Thorn there,' she pointed out deliberately. 'I like to use beautiful things every day, no matter how grand. I'm sure Thorn won't have any objection.'

'My own view is exactly the opposite to that!' Maggie bit off with some asperity, determined to make a good fight of it.

'My nephew cares a great deal about our possessions, I assure you. He's by no means as whimsical as all that. How foolish of you to imagine it, but you don't know my nephew half so well as you think. If you can't or won't learn that by yourself, my telling you might save valuable time. A lot of things in this life are illusion, no more real than the mirage in the desert. One may follow it, certainly, but it's only atmospheric effect.'

'None the less beautiful for all that!' Katia said, and

turned slowly, her blue gown brushed with violet, swirling about her feet, her throat rising like the stem of a flower, from the deep ruffled V of the bodice. 'You look very well,' she said carefully into the fraught silence. 'I've always liked that dress.' Her tone and her manner implied that she meant just that, for the dress was, in its way, superb, dateless and cut by a master hand, but Maggie chose to misinterpret.

'It pains me to mention it, but I find you just that bit ... overdressed!' she said callously. 'Stagy.'

Acting under some foreign impulse, for something quite different sprang to mind, Katia gave a little laugh. 'Nonsense, Maggie! I can't take that seriously at all. My couturier would be horrified. Besides, Mother gets so much pleasure out of my appearance, dressing up if you like, I put it on mainly to please her. The sapphires were Thorn's twenty-first birthday gift, as you know. I hope I'm forgiven for that!'

'More accurately I could never be persuaded that you deserved them!' Maggie answered dryly, 'but I've learnt to make allowances.' Her strong brows stayed level, always fresh for a new thrust. 'I would strongly advise you, however, to hide your hopeless passion for my nephew from your Ivor d'Arcy. Whatever else he is, the man's not a fool! I've caught the odd look here and there and he's only been in the house twenty-four hours. If you're not a little more constrained in your behaviour you'll draw a blank all round. This man is one of your own kind. Perhaps you can give him happiness!' Wearily Maggie looked up, as thought the slightest contact of their incompatible personalities tired her out, throwing up as it did such unpleasantness. 'You've never been able to fool me,' she said, 'that's why you've got nothing to say for yourself now, though with your odd way of life, one might have expected some slick response. The thing is, *I* have no need to make excuses for myself. I was born on Carunya. I'm a McCabe with all that entails and I hope to die here. There never was and there never will be room for both of us. Some things one must just accept. Your mother is quite different. In a way I'm quite fond of her, and her illness and the splendid way she's fought back has made me more fond. The children are, of course, McCabes, a part of my beloved brother.'

'Yes, indeed!' Katia agreed with an aloof and desperate kind of humour. Ridiculous to be hurt over and over again. 'I find it hard to believe you've ever been fond of anyone, Maggie. Your heart is an old, cold stone!' The sense of reopening all the old wounds came on her, driving her, but Maggie's voice conveyed that she found the remark trite and meaningless.

'That was worthy of you, my dear, but at least we understand one another. I can even appreciate the torment you must be suffering. My advice to you, and you would be wise to exercise it, is: cut short your mistakes. Marry your theatrical friend. Crying after the moon won't earn you one atom of commiseration round here. Thorn is proud of his name as I am. When the time comes he will marry into a family like our own, landed people who know what is expected of them.'

'You will allow him to marry, then?' Katia inquired, opening her blue eyes wider. 'That's very generous of you!'

'And a lot sooner than you think!' Maggie said with a strange, bitter expression. 'You surely didn't think the Dickinsons were invited for nothing!' She added, glancing up, her eyes gleaming: 'Don't think so badly of me, child. I'm merely doing my duty as I see it. I'm actually helping you to see yours. You've no money to fall back on, so you can't sacrifice your career for one silly whim. Have you no pride, that you cling like a schoolgirl to your hero-worship? You'd better settle it once and for all. There's little point in covering yourself with ridicule, and that's all that remains to you. I've done all *I* can. Mr. d'Arcy seems the ideal way out of the difficulty. It may just possibly be the making of you, then you can go your own way as usual. Your mother is doing splendidly now and you can rely on us here at Carunya to see she will continue to be well looked after. We manage quite nicely, you know, when you're not around!'

'I imagine so!' Katia looked back at the older woman steadily, wondering how she could ever have aroused such enmity and coldly amused vehemence. 'It's even possible to gain a certain sober hilarity from you, Maggie. The best character actress I know wouldn't have a chance with you. In your own way you're superb, only they don't write lines like that any more — fling the truth and the near truth in people's faces like so much wet rag adding gloom to the evening with your prophecies and judgments. What more could I ask?'

'Go away and I'll never bother you again!' Maggie answered with a harsh little laugh. The magnificent emerald in its old-fashioned setting flashed from her hand.

The green eye of malevolence! Katia thought, trying not to cry. Did she really expect everyone to love her? 'Why have you always hated me, Maggie?' she asked with something of the pained wonder of her childhood. 'And *hate* it is, I realize that now. It's gone way beyond simple antagonism!'

The 'eye' glittered in the light, and Maggie gave an odd, unlovely laugh. 'To make the fantastic obvious, I don't really know. You've always irritated me excessively. Certainly I've never been so keenly aware of anyone else's defects. Now, as you say, it's something else again. But hear this, whatever else I'm not sure about, I'm sure of this: You're not a quarter good enough for my nephew, and there's no way to remedy that!' The sombre eyes were unnaturally bright in the set, white face. The tall figure invested with a terrible majesty. The large, shapely hand lay calmly in her lap, but the mouth was set in a tight line.

'Perhaps your warnings are unnecessary,' Katia pointed out, her whole body controlled, only the wild rose colour in her cheeks to show for the passion and humiliated anguish throbbing inside her. 'It's just possible I realize I've found my true vocation, the only thing I'm fitted for – my career. I'm a good actress!'

'No actress is a lady, though some of them give a very passable imitation!' Maggie intoned with the air of a woman of impeccable repute, whose every sentence was significant, bound in gold, unspeakably cruel to her own sex.

Not surprisingly Katia laughed, with her deep sense of the ridiculous – a young sound, golden and melodic. 'I'm immensely grateful not many people think like that. As a matter of fact, Maggie, your conversation would be rather irksome in urban society. The more charitable would put it down to your rather solitary way of life!'

This seemed to push Maggie to the edge of cold fury. 'You were always outrageously insolent,' she said tightly, 'and you may continue to be so. For your mother's sake I'm prepared to avoid friction. Our quarrel will continue as it has always done – in silence. *You* know and *I* know I've guessed your secret. Rather, I've always known what one day it would be. My solitary life has made me acutely observant, if nothing else!' Her light eyes, contemptuous and morose, ranged over Katia's fragile grace. 'I'll say this for you, you've learnt how to handle yourself. So tiresome, all those tantrums and none to back you up. Not for us to make a scene like some hired help from the kitchen. At least we've taught you that!' As she spoke, her voice grew very dry. 'I shall only say again with sufficient emphasis because you've been overlong in coming to this, there *is* no place for you on Carunya. You may set the rest of the world on fire if you wish, but out here all your little schemes will fall flat, flat, flat!'

'All our conversations are rather horrible!' Katia said quietly, her eyes matching the brilliance of the sapphires.

'As long as they're not futile!' Maggie countered in a hard, metallic tone. 'You surely don't think I've no eyes in my head? I've seen how you've been these past two weeks, hanging on Thorn's every word. You can't take your eyes off him, and you're utterly unsuited to one another. Only Thorn's strong sense of duty and your mother's presence here has kept you together. But it's no longer convenient. It's time now for Thorn to consider marriage. He must have an heir, and he's thirty-five years old!'

'Not quite at the end of his resources!' Katia said

flippantly over her disordered heart, but Maggie sensed her tormented nerves.

'Too bad!' she said with impersonal fairness, 'but no one's making you drink poison. If you thought you were going to miss out on a few cold facts, then you're a fool. After all, you must expect that!'

'Oh yes, I do,' Katia said with an ironic little smile. 'It's your task, somehow. One way and the other, Maggie, you've done a good deal of harm.'

'But this is going to be different, and I've sufficient say in the matter to finish the job!'

Katia felt her throat close. Even the smell of the flowers seemed unbearable. Fear was the enemy and some part of her, the child, still went in fear and trepidation of Maggie. Kindness could be met with kindness, but Maggie had never offered her that, only the empty vessel of spite and hostility. Maggie, like a powerful animal to the challenge, was breathing hard and fast, but Katia more than ever thought such emotions a stain and a blemish. She would not permit herself to continue the encounter.

She turned sideways, her face a pure, pale mask in the brilliant glow from the chandelier, all her senses gathered for the effort.

'I must go and see after Mother.'

'I was going to suggest it!' Maggie answered with vicious good humour, the long fingers of one hand cramped tightly into the palm, extraordinarily controlled in the face of the girl's hardly sufferable beauty.

Chin lifted, Katia walked swiftly out of the room, in her sea-coloured dress, her eyes dense blue between their thick, heavy lashes. The blood thundered in her veins, coursing like fire. Every word that Maggie had said chimed in her head. She had come face to face with all her illusions, thick as the sands of the sea. Was it true she knew little of Thorn and less of herself? She could still feel his mouth on her own, stealing her breath, a wildfire within her. But Maggie had flung the truth in her face. It was the first time; and the last.

Dinner was served in the formal dining-room reserved by the family for entertaining. The informal dining-room, overlooking the terraced gardens to the rear of the house, was considered far more practical for everyday use. And small wonder! Ivor thought, his respectful eye roving the height and graceful proportions of the serenely beautiful room. Quite a few valuable antiques were housed there from the collection started by Duncan McCabe, the present McCabe's great-grandfather. According to a family biography published a few years back, Duncan McCabe had been a man possessed of an infallible flair for distinguishing between genuine and fake. A passionate collector and something of a financial wizard, for not only had he provided for the continuing pleasure of his family and heirs, a beautiful, harmonious background for living, but he made a great deal of money on the side when his own home had reached saturation point. A few of his notable contemporaries, hellbent on another route, had volunteered their opinion of his interest in 'knick-knacks' as lunatic, but his wife came to his defence with the observation that it was a far safer pastime than chasing horses or women.

The result, so far as Ivor was concerned, was that

Carunya was one of the most beautiful and livable houses he had ever been in. Occasionally Ivor went on an antique safari himself. Money was the problem, but obviously not here. Still, he had one or two nice things himself. With something like envy he viewed the rich antique walnut of the dining table and chairs, the wall cabinets, holding the best pieces from a collection of hard paste porcelain, both Western and Oriental. A superb crystal and bronze dore chandelier blazed overhead. On the long, traditional buffet was a Georgian silver service flanked by a pair of two light candelabra of elegant design, all reflected in a giltwood mirror which might or might not have been Chippendale. But the thing that tantalized his eye, softly lit in one corner, was a beautiful gilt bronze figure of a young girl, a masterpiece of sensitive, refined sensuality. He would have given a great deal to own that, for somehow it reminded him of Katia. Later on McCabe admitted to having paid far too much for it on his last trip abroad for just that reason. Happily, for his digestion, Ivor didn't know that then, never being a man to disregard the significance of anything.

For the moment he was very content. A civilized place indeed, he thought, as he enjoyed the pronounced bouquet and soft finish of his dry red wine. He had been trying with little success to lay down a small quantity of that particular vintage since it had been released commercially. It was superb already, almost a pity to drink it, but he knew for a fact that McCabe had plenty more of it in the excellent cellar he had been shown over yesterday. Ivor saw no reason not to polish it off, contemplating the luxurious night-time leisure of the great station. A world apart really with the vast wilderness, a great desert and a blazing sun at its door.

And McCabe! Ivor stole another narrow glance at his host. Handsome, certainly, with authority hammered out all over the dark, chiselled face. An intellect Ivor could admire and recognize, an inherited awareness for beauty in all its forms, yet he was totally related to his background, still representing great style. Almost with something of his famous thoroughbreds, Ivor thought, the same lines, the same dash, the same spirit. Good blood. Good breeding, he supposed. Whatever it was it showed.

Sensing this regard, on a wavelength of his own, McCabe turned his head, throwing Ivor a faint, courteous smile. Ivor felt his skin prickle. The latent look of power and perception in those brilliant black eyes was an actual force, leadership plainly in them. Well, he was a king of a kind, Ivor reasoned, feeling vaguely exposed, with all the position's attendant duties and responsibilities. He wouldn't care to take it on, he had enough on his hands just looking after himself.

Slightly flurried, but hiding it easily, Ivor let his gaze slip over to the old aunt. Miss Maggie McCabe, and thank God for it! She would have given any man a rare old dance! A formidable old girl to be sure, sitting very straight in her chair, pleasant enough for the most part, eating and drinking with great confidence and a restrained kind of enjoyment, not really caring how anyone else was faring.

They were faring very well, Ivor thought dryly, speculating on the past courses. Halved avocados in lettuce cups, filled with oysters flown in from the Gulf, spooned over with a really superb dressing – he would have to find out what it was. The superb fillet of Carunya beef in a flaky cheese pastry served with garden-fresh minted potatoes, little carrots, green peas and the tossed salad he liked so much. The chocolate rum cream concoction he had passed up in favour of the cheese platter and the rest of the wine. Miss McCabe, he noticed, did justice to both and drank champagne throughout. No one else felt so inclined, with a choice of two excellent whites and the incomparable Cabernet.

They were very fortunate in having plenty of help. Ivor smiled graciously at the dusky little belle who was removing his plate. There were two of them, rising splendidly to the occasion, as silent and decorative as two velvety brown moths with touches of colour in their neat, becoming uniforms with cream collars and cuffs. His regard, at needle point, settled first and last on Katia. He would have been blind not to notice the sudden, odd heightening of her beauty, so who knew what spells lay in her.

The glow from the chandelier washed over her face and bare shoulders, the lovely chiffon dress, her eyes the same smoky lavender blue, as dazzling in their fashion as the sun on the sea. The black hair, the brows, the thick, heavy smudge of lashes, were brilliant foils for her gardenia-pale skin. But here now was a face Ivor had never seen and he had the dismal notion that he wasn't the cause of it. The two young stepsisters, whom he liked very much, for all their golden young radiance paled into insignificance beside the Katia they loved so much.

His eyes moved on with real admiration to Mrs. Carole McCabe, seated at the opposite end of the table to her stepson, in her every look and gesture towards him a strange touching trust and affection. She was understandably frailer than the last time Ivor had seen her, but the doctor's report on her progress was most heartening. It heartened Ivor too, for any number of reasons. The main one he would explain to Katia tonight, judging his first evening on Carunya to have been too soon. Tonight, Mrs. McCabe looked so much better, wearing a softly tailored satin suit with an exquisite diamond sunburst on one lapel. The gentle smile on her face seemed to Ivor to express her personality beautifully.

The other guests for the evening were long-time family friends, the Dickinsons. The father, obviously well-to-do, a bit of a bore but a nice fellow for all that. The wife, much younger, one of those brittle, faintly malicious society women Ivor knew well and detested, though they were meat and drink to him in his business. The daughter, just back from an extended tour of Europe and the States, was not noticeably related to either of them. She was a very attractive young woman, taller than average, might run to fat later on, but a good body now, a chic dresser, the face nothing stirring but with a clean-cut look of health, good skin and lovely teeth, that was very appealing. Liz was her name and it suited her, an uncomplicated, outgoing personality. It would have been glaringly apparent to a blind man in blinkers that she was 'gone' on McCabe. All through dinner, which she indulged in with youthful abandon, she rattled on non-stop, when the mother wasn't, her conversation surface but sparkling, directed in the main to McCabe. But he was a very cool customer indeed, Ivor thought, one part of him drawn to the man. One got the certain feeling there had been plenty of attractive girls before Liz. But what after? That was the knife in Ivor's heart and he was sufficiently theatrical to think of it as just that.

Mrs. Dickinson for some reason of her own was calling into question the authenticity of a large French tapestry that hung in unchallenged splendour on one wall. Miss McCabe hardly broke the glide of her wineglass to her mouth to assure her in a minimum of words that this wasn't so. Only Ivor caught the amused, private glance that passed between two pairs of eyes, the way McCabe raised his wineglass very slightly in intimate salute.

All that sex appeal and money as well! There was no justice anywhere, Ivor thought, deeply disturbed. These brilliant little cameos had to stop. The whole table was no more than a theatre in the round, with McCabe charming the whole damn lot of them into his camp. Liz Dickinson continued to bubble, cramming into one evening all the feverish abandon she might have spread over the past eighteen months. She was full of enthusiasm, her energy and eagerness such, Ivor felt if he didn't get away presently he would be sapped of all strength. Miss Maggie McCabe joined them for coffee around an exquisite Chinese table, her disposition as charming as her character allowed, her wintry smiles joyfully reflected in Mrs. Dickinson's eyes with a message that made Ivor's heart ache over. Like the very best conversationalists, Ivor was given over a great deal to listening, and so was McCabe, a certain sardonic amusement in the depths of his slanting black eyes.

It was a good hour later before Ivor had Katia to himself, and guided her out on to the moon-drenched terrace, heavy with the scent of the native boronia. From somewhere beyond the lagoon a shivery, beautiful woman chant throbbed in the star-spangled darkness, softly supported by the spirit drums. It was plaintive and rather primitive and Ivor felt an eerie shiver run down his spine. Beyond the perimeter of the homestead proper, the amber and rose gold lights of the house, the twinkling 'eyes' of the satellite buildings, who knew what lay out there. It was almost like visiting another planet, Ivor thought, perhaps a little uneasy in his unfamiliar environment; not realizing he was coming under the strange influence of the limitless Outback with its Dreamtime traditions and Stone Age rituals. Forbidding country, he decided, and absolutely fatal to the careless traveller.

Tonight, as last night, the stars were incredibly large and brilliant, blazing like white flowers, sown thickly into the purplish black tapestry of night-messengers for young lovers, according to the aborigines, so Katia told him. The strange, unnatural singing persisted, wafting across the tree tops, in places oddly off key, a whispery sound that was also strong and sweet. Ivor shifted his position a little restlessly. Exposed to this kind of thing too long he would probably break out in goose pimples. He didn't have the nervous system to absorb all this tribal psyche thing.

In the dark and terrible days of the 'Storm Bird', the bloody war between the white intruder and the aboriginal defender of the sacred hunting grounds, many shocking massacres had occurred around here. A lot of blood, black and white, had soaked into the ancient ground. It gave off an atmosphere, to Ivor, at any rate. He looked across at Katia's perfect profile, tilted towards the sky. This kind of thing obviously had great charm for her. It was part of her heritage too, he supposed.

She turned to smile at him softly, twisting his heart. 'The tribal sky gods! See how they sweep in so close to the sweet, spicy earth. Sirius, mighty hunter, carrying his bright touch to light up the Dreamtime paths. What are you thinking about, Ivor?'

'Need you ask?' He made a small gesture towards her, to draw her back gently into his arms, feeling the warm living scent of her. His heart gave a loud single beat and he moved his mouth over the soft silk of her throat. 'How I've missed you! God, how I've missed you! Damn silly really, when you don't appear to have given me a single thought.'

'Not true!'

'The only method of dealing with that is to carry you off.' He touched her arm and turned her to him. 'Kiss me, darling, seeing I have to beg!' His light, ironic voice broke off abruptly as he lowered his head with unshakeable purpose. 'I am honoured indeed!' he murmured against her mouth, for once determined to use a little force. These Snow White tactics had to stop. 'Don't retreat, darling,' he said deliberately, 'you're being pursued!'

Her eyes closed, Katia turned up her face, outwardly submissive, inwardly a mumble of uneasy emotions. She longed to be free, yet felt chained by her very real affection for him. Affection wasn't love and never grew to be, she realized that now. But Ivor had given her much. She surrendered as though she was repaying some indefinable debt.

Driven by the forces gathering in him, stubbornly

blind to it, Ivor kissed her long and hard, glorying in the joy of her sweetness and tenderness, the ecstasy that surely would one day come. With a movement on the surface, perfectly easy, he let her go, his hands coming down flat on her shoulders, trembling slightly. The eyes that opened to him, in the light, so blazingly blue, now shimmered like crystals. 'Come and sit down, darling,' he said, taking her hand and drawing her into the glimmering shadows of the cushioned swing.

Katia drew a funny little breath and tried to relax.

'When are you coming back with me?' Ivor asked, his eyes on the subtle amethyst in the sky.

'I can't say right now. Please don't ask me, Ivor. Mother is so much better, but I feel far from happy about leaving her for some little while.'

'Perhaps my news might persuade you!' Ivor countered. As the words left him he had the bleak notion that it might not. 'I'm going to the States,' he announced into the velvety obscurity. 'Cy Wagner has offered me a script-writing job with his own outfit. The contract is as good as signed. I only waited to tell you.'

This awoke Katia to sudden life. 'Hollywood?' she said like a passionate child. 'But we need you here, Ivor. You're our most gifted playwright. We can't afford to lose you!'

'From the tone of your voice, dear, one might have thought I said Hades!'

'But Hollywood, Ivor! They have plenty of professional writers who can handle that type of thing. You're for the theatre, distinguished already. You can come up with big things!'

'And who's going to pay me big money in the meantime?' Ivor inquired. 'You know yourself, darling, I'm on a miserable retainer. It's a wonder I survive at all. Coming out here and seeing all this has decided me. I want money, lots of it. I wasn't born like McCabe to inherit wealth. I've succeeded by myself. It's early days for the arts here and I'm no pioneer. The thing is, I've been offered a job at an astronomical salary and I'd be the biggest goat in the world to refuse. I can always work away at my own stuff on the side. Wagner wants to meet you as well. He hasn't seen you work, of course, but he's seen nearly all your publicity photographs. You're wonderfully photogenic. It doesn't always follow even with really good-looking girls. Who knows what name you could make for yourself? Perhaps you're a shade too "Englishified" – his own word, for the American palate, but other ladylike types have made it. Wagner thought you rather recalled the young Vivien Leigh!'

'If I could *act* like her I'd be satisfied!' Katia said, suddenly taciturn. 'I don't want to be a film star, Ivor, even in the unlikely event that I *could* make it. One doesn't have to be an actress to succeed in films, as you've said more than once to me in the past. The public, en masse, just have to accept you – sex appeal and all that!'

'Well, you've plenty of that!' Ivor began dryly. 'Don't kid yourself. Really, darling, you overdo this underselling yourself. Plenty of cool types have succeeded. You should glory in your talent instead of putting yourself down. A little more drive, self-confidence is needed. Together we could take on the whole world, with the chance of real money. I'm sick to death of buttering up rich old girls who wouldn't know *King Lear* from a wayward farce! They're too thick on the ground. I want to be my own man!'

'It could be a journey into nothingness,' she said slowly. 'The life might not suit you at all. You might find yourself and your own gift gobbled up. I'm certain the place would devour me!'

He turned on her with the sense of irritation a kernel of truth finds. 'You know, Katy, sometimes I get the feeling you're not ambitious at all!'

'Perhaps I'm not! It's a thought increasingly in my mind of late!'

Swiftly Ivor made a volte-face, tracing his thumb over her palm. 'It's your mother's illness, darling. It's unsettled you badly, as well it might. I know how much you mean to one another. Won't you at least meet Wagner? It's no small thing for a big American pro- ducer to be willing to meet you. In his business beauti- ful girls are the rule, not the exception. He's up at the Reef for another week, big game fishing, having a whale of a time. They haven't got anything like that over there!'

Somewhere in the garden of diffused radiance, a bird began to sing – a lovely throbbing line, immeasur- ably sad. Ivor very nearly put it to flight, his voice suddenly explosive.

'God, what's wrong with that bird? It sounds like a lover who knows its love's hopeless!'

Katia didn't answer. She couldn't. The liquid anguished warbling contained all the pity of love in the world. Suddenly the song gave way to silence. Katia's own nerves felt tautened.

'It's such a gamble, Ivor! I can't think of you over

there. I know you need fresh experience, time off to experiment, but you have a point to make here – in your plays!'

He sighed, 'You're a problem child yourself, Kate. You're an uncomfortably good actress with the real knack of getting under the skin of the part, yet you reject a chance at the front rank. It doesn't add up!'

'No woman adds up all that well!' she said quite seriously. 'I could act all my life and what is left? Where are the children? I want children of my own to love. Do you?'

Manlike, Ivor spoke the unvarnished truth. 'I can't say I've given any thought to it. But I'm prepared to give you any blessed thing you want. We'll have a whole dozen if you like. But what of your career? It rarely mixes with motherhood, or not more than one or two at the outside. You told me once that to act was your life's mission!'

'I thought so at the time. We all have to try these things to find out if they're true – sometimes with the utmost pain and trouble. The real joke is, Ivor, lately even my acting has become mechanical!'

He couldn't repress his exclamation of annoyance. 'You're too hard on yourself, darling, a perfectionist. You're the finest young actress I know – and that's Ivor d'Arcy, leading light, speaking, not the man who is lamentably crazy about you. Not even love could blind me to your shortcomings in that regard. By the way, my sweet, this conversation is slightly grating after such a superb dinner. I thought you'd be thrilled with my big chance. Yours too, if you want it!'

She reached up and kissed his cheek. 'I'm very happy for you, Ivor, if you are. As for myself, I'd be hopelessly out of my element in a celluloid world.'

'Is it possible you're timid?' he inquired gently. 'Frightened to take the plunge? I know you're no Raquel Welch, but no one's asking you to be that, for God's sake, least of all me. As far as that goes, you can give up acting altogether and devote yourself to looking after me. I'd love that, and I shall do my level best to fill the house with little ones. The sad part is I don't think you want that, either. In short, my darling, I don't know *what* you want, and I'm pretty damned sure you don't either!'

'We're not quarrelling, are we?' she asked affectionately. 'You've such a lovely clear voice with all that training. It does carry, you know!'

'The old girl's all for me!' Ivor announced with some satisfaction.

'Maggie? How on earth does she know? Surely you didn't tell her?'

'The Maggies of this world don't have to be told. They have their own inbuilt antennae. I would say, at a guess, Miss Maggie McCabe is definitely on my side. The sooner I carry you off to some foreign clime the better. Strange, with all your conquests, but I don't think you've made a fan there, my love. But one can't win 'em all. It's my own private view that women are awful bitches to one another. Your Miss Maggie McCabe lost no time in conveying her sentiments without a word. Your childhood has been chock-a-block with incidents. A conspirator in the grand tradition. Been one all her life, I'd say!'

'You're the first one to say that!' Katia laughed a little helplessly.

'I have a rare gift like some very old Tibetan lama.

Besides, you're dearer to me than life itself. It makes me more sensitive – *and* I'm a realist, which you're not. You'll push no claims out here, not with the Queen of Hearts around. She would have your head with quite unseemly speed – a quick, dainty death. I could never live comfortably with her myself. A funny one for McCabe to have as an aunt. He has enough charm to make Bonnie Prince Charlie look tawdry!'

It took Katia a few moments to realize she was being challenged. 'You talk as if you don't really like him, when I know you do!'

'Which just goes to show my immense moral stature!' Ivor said dryly. 'Thorn McCabe is a fine man, I'm forced to admit it.' In the soft darkness he found her two hands and brought them up to his mouth to kiss the fingertips. 'But he's not for you, Katia. You're mine, and I'll put up a fight!' His hands, as controlled as his voice, pushed up her head. 'Don't play the innocent with me, Kate. You're half-way in love with him, always have been, I suppose, and being the man I am, I can understand it so long as it stops now. For one thing, you'll never be considered his equal by Aunty. She has no intention of relinquishing her stranglehold on the old plantation.'

'She has no claim on the house,' Katia pointed out quietly. 'Thorn owns it outright.'

'You surely don't imagine he'd kick her out? Not McCabe. Not a man like that. Only one glimpse is enough to assure you of that. She's family – a tiresome old girl, certainly, and ageing, but *family*. A lady of the Court, no less. I've often heard that these big holdings are run like castles, and it's no exaggeration. Chivalry is in full flower out here. You'd better come back with me before the wind changes. Miss Maggie McCabe is long accustomed to getting what she wants, and from what I've seen tonight, in her frosty, button-lip fashion, she's given the all-clear to the local girl. Unlike you, Liz Dickinson will have no quarrel there, and who's to say Maggie's not right? After all, Liz does know what it's all about. An ideal choice in a way!' An odd expression, half understanding, half rueful, rested on Ivor's face. 'Don't let me hurt you, darling. Let me save you. Be quite sure I would never have brought the subject up if I didn't consider it necessary. I've a heart like a baby, especially where you're concerned.'

From inside the house came a high merry peal of laughter. 'Liz, being irresistibly drawn to the local lord of creation!' Ivor observed rather sourly.

'It won't be the first time or the last!'

'I've no doubt!' Ivor's voice grew even drier. 'He's an extremely attractive man. Almost a revelation. Small wonder you ran away!'

'I didn't run away,' Katia said quietly, all trace of colour washed out of her voice.

'Didn't you? I see now quite clearly it was a defence mechanism. But consider, my little love, dominant males like McCabe sometimes turn to empty-headed heiresses, all frivolity.'

'I'd say there was a great deal more to Liz than that. She's over-excited tonight. Carunya has gone to her head, like champagne. It can have that effect!'

Ivor turned to her with a little mocking noise that was still admiring. 'I like you, Kate. I like you very much, added to which I am madly in love with you – a problem all round. Come with me, darling. I'm sick of playing Pinocchio, strings pulled all round, no matter how cleverly. We'll give it a go, and if we don't like it we can always come home. I'd never allow you to become unhappy. You can't really know until you try a thing if you'll like it or not. Don't be so set in your mind. You have to escape this deep involvement with McCabe, Carunya. It's fatal. You've got to push on and out to new experiences, new people.'

'Substitutes, you mean?' she said with an exquisite little smile as sad as anything he'd seen.

'Don't say that!' he cautioned her, plainly not to be put off. 'You mustn't even allow yourself to think like that, otherwise you'll never uproot yourself. It's a big wide world, bigger than the boundaries of Carunya. You've lived this part through and through. Chase a phantom and you'll miss the real thing. Me, I love you. Can I say more? More important, has McCabe ever said it? I know quite well he hasn't. Poor little Katia and a man like McCabe! No wonder you're hiding a few lacerations.'

Katia shivered and tilted her head back, letting a cool stream of air play over her face and throat. Lacerations, she thought, and shied away from the word passionately. No, never that. Thorn had a deep vein of compassion that cut close to the heart but never left scars. Through all her humours and odd bursts of temperament he had been unfailingly firm but kind. She could never forget that. What had Thorn said to her: A little love given and taken lived forever in the memory. Why should she try to smother what she felt for him like a new skill undertaken?

As though he caught the very drift of her thoughts, Ivor grasped her shoulders, lightly shook them. 'Give this some serious thought, Kate. A few days, then I'll want your answer. I have my own pride. Your black hair, and your starry eyes and your head tilted away from me – even if I lost you I'd regret nothing. You've touched something deep in me, no other woman has ever touched before, and never will again. I'll remember everything!'

Her breath came in a short, distressed little gasp. 'But I could never forget you either. Not that I would want to.' She was as solemn, as serious as a child, her deep distaste for hurting anyone, anything, plainly showing. A man could take advantage of that if he so desired, Ivor thought, abandoning the idea with quick regret. He cared too much about her for emotional blackmail.

'Blessed are the merciful, for mercy they shall find!' he said quietly, looking into her limpid eyes. 'Cheer up, darling, in a moment we'll be singing Auld Lang Syne!' He half turned his head, his voice changing into one of amused surprise. 'Heavens, that's not the good Miss McCabe like some hunting cat behind the shades? It is, how refreshing! I didn't think she'd stoop to anything so commonplace. On the other hand she could be checking me out. I think she sees all her guests as friendly burglars.' He slid an arm along the back of Katia's shoulders and pressed a kiss on her cheek. 'There, that's for Maggie's benefit. God knows she deserves a few hopeful signs . . . So in the end, Katy,' he returned to his contemplative style, 'we're back where we started, this interminable see-sawing up and down. Will she or won't she give me an answer? I've never thought about it before, but it's a humiliating experience, loving. An idea I'm working on now. You can't imagine how frozen with longing and loneliness I've been these past few weeks – absolute anguish. The extraordinary part is, I work better that way. The pain seems to stiffen me up, puts a fine edge on my sensibilities!'

'A new play?' Katia cut in on him, alerted to the professional note in his voice.

Ivor nodded his head, not beyond being thrilled by that lovely, lilting note of interest and pride. 'I won't tell you how good it is. I'll let you find out for yourself. I suppose eventually you'll want a share of the takings. A lot of it is you!'

Katia digested this in silence, not without humour, knowing that even in his most extravagant moments Ivor never failed to retain the third eye of the creative artist. 'You know, darling,' she said lightly, 'I think every experience is just copy for you. You research everyone you meet, good and bad. You have this marvellous detachment even when you're passionately and personally involved. I don't think you love me at all. I'm just your kind of heroine!'

He laughed a little at the impact of that. 'I'll let the indictment stand. You *are* my type of heroine! You come first to my mind every time. But the real test of whether you're my kind of woman is the wonderful feelings you arouse in me, the heart and the mind, so that you're never far from my consciousness. You see, I really believe that at the ripe old age of thirty-eight there *is* only one love of your life. Any number of love affairs if you've the mind or the time. Precious few take hold of the imagination, live as strongly over time and distance. I'm completely alive with you, and without you from now on, I'll be on my own. Fortunately I can live with loneliness, even turn it to good effect. I suppose you could call me one of the lucky ones!'

'You're my dearest friend and colleague!' Katia said with a smile in her voice, and pressed against his arm. 'We're all going to be very proud of you!'

'A living legend!' Ivor returned very dryly, and dropped a kiss on her silky head. Was it the wind that set the curtains stirring? He said practically over his shoulder for the benefit of anyone who might be listening, 'Shall we take a walk in the garden? I feel magnificently lightheaded after what you've told me!'

It would be easier to have a fight with a face in a mirror than embarrass Miss Maggie McCabe, Ivor thought wryly. She had every degree of self-esteem there was. Still, one couldn't help trying. Katia with her quick perceptions and deep sense of humour played up to him beautifully. Together, arm in arm, they sauntered down the wide shallow steps, exquisitely frivolous, deliciously brittle, like a Noël Coward couple. Katia, Ivor recalled, for all her passion and fire in drama, really did shine in these roles!

CHAPTER SEVEN

A CHAIR away, Katia tried closing her mind to the sound of Liz's voice. She had thought several times of making an excuse and going inside, but decided against it, in case she gave even the slightest offence. In any case, her mother didn't appear to mind the conversational meandering through a bewildering number of subjects, her low soft gurgle of laughter coming whenever Liz said something funny, which Katia had to admit was pretty frequently.

Liz was lying back on the cushioned recliner, her brown eyes glowing, showing vast amounts of beautifully tanned skin, with only a token wisp of black jersey bikini, the bra gathered into a gold ring and held by a thin halter. She was in wonderful shape, and clearly felt she owed it to the rest of them not to keep the fact secret. Her cover-up kimono jacket, the same lime green as her enormous floppy beach hat, lay a safe distance away, as cool and untouched as a leafy splash in a rain forest.

The glitter off the pool struck at Katia's eyes right through her huge tortoiseshell sunglasses. In the aquamarine depths Susan and Debby were gliding and performing like seals, tossing a coloured beach ball at one another. Carole had taken her dip earlier and was resting in the combined shade of a blossoming gum and the striped umbrella. She felt suspended, weightless and happy in the warm open air with the children she loved so much around her. As she sipped at the cool drink Sarah had left her, she listened to Liz's chatter which her own mother had abandoned long ago, going indoors to the study, claiming the need to dash off a few letters. The Dickinsons were staying on a few days after Ivor d'Arcy's departure, giving the distinct impression that important decisions were in the air.

Katia, with her matt creamy white skin, that would not take the sun, lifted the blue straw hat from her head and looked briefly around. Nothing had changed. Liz put down a bottle of body oil and smiled:

'Say, you're a real hothouse flower, aren't you?'

'Guaranteed to expire at the first kiss of the sun. I envy you your beautiful tan, Liz. It's fantastically becoming!' It was too, with Liz's arm brown eyes and short glossy tapering head of curls. Katia did not say that for her own part she would have felt happier with weights attached to that brief black bikini lest the wind take it, but Liz, with considerable unabashed vanity, looked down at her own body.

'Straight as an arrow with all the curves in the right places – that's me! But I've planned early, I'll tell you!'

'We've noticed, dear!' Carole said with real humour and not a particle of reproof in her voice. 'You look delightful. I have to take the sun in measured doses myself and Katia just doesn't tan at all. She's never even had a freckle so far as I can recall. Shawn, my first husband, had skin like that.'

Liz braced her long slender feet against the end of the raised redwood decking just out of splashing distance of the pool. She stretched luxuriously three times, then began to slowly raise and lower her hips. 'I work frightfully hard to keep this shape,' she announced blithely, 'but nothing like so hard as Mother. What that woman endures, all to fit into size twelve! She nearly killed herself a few years back, but I suppose I shouldn't be telling you that. Fluid pills — nearly dehydrated herself. I'm going to give it all away myself when I hit forty!'

'Then expect to have your marriage threatened!' Carole counselled her unexpectedly. 'One must always take care.'

'So where does a girl stand?' Liz asked wryly. 'I do so love food!'

'Doesn't everybody? It's certainly something to think about.'

'Don't you believe it!' Liz flipped over on her tummy. 'I flatted with a girl overseas who literally found it repulsive. And that's a fairly recent, utterly true experience!'

'I'll bet she had all sorts of ailments!' said Carole, brushing a spent leaf off her head. 'When a person eats too much there's a reason, often psychological, and needless to say the same applies when one can't or won't take adequate nourishment.'

'Well, I'm always hungry,' Liz said matter-of-factly, 'and I'm a person who likes to be straight and clear about myself. I don't hide anything to impress anyone.'

'I should say *not*!' Carole essayed with a smiling, pointed little inclination of her head.

'Naughty, Carole, but you've forgotten what it's like — the social scene, I mean. It's a battlefield, and the body beautiful is armour. My mother and a lot of her friends don't feel secure unless they're thin. They chase the pounds like an ardent greyhound after a mechanical rabbit. They've *got* to wear their clothes properly. Mother spends a small fortune on clothes. I do myself, but now and then I wonder why. This body image business is too severe – committing yourself to an army of faceless, fashionable clothes-horses. Take you and Katia, you're petite types, small-boned, rather fragile. You'll probably be exactly the same as old ladies. You don't have Mother's and my troubles at all. We're big-boned, the fatal flaw. It's an endless war to keep slim. What happens when I have children and the metabolism gets shaken upside down! Mother refused point-blank to have any more after me – a fact all too true, ask Dad, even if Mother has chosen to forget it. She's made a real problem for herself and our way of life doesn't help. I'd like to get out of it. I've seen all there is to see and now I'd like to settle down. I hope to pretty soon. I'm not going to have my life style cramped. This kind of life suits me better, the great outdoors. Plenty of fresh air and exercise. One could ride it off!' She turned her artlessly artful brown eyes on Katia. 'I like your Ivor! He's a wonderfully witty man, very easy to talk to. I thought he might be fearfully erudite. If he tilts his head to a particular angle he reminds me a bit of that English actor – what was his name? – Guy Rolfe. It must be wonderful to have such a great common bond. Real communication is so terribly important, don't you think? When are you getting married?' she asked without waiting for an answer. 'I'm not guessing entirely, Maggie made some mention of the subject after breakfast this morning.'

'Perhaps you'd better ask Maggie, then!' Katia returned lightly, exchanging eye signals with her mother. 'I'm none too sure myself. Ivor is my good friend, Liz.

I'm not thinking of him in terms of anything else at the moment.'

'Good heavens, I've been misled!' Liz said shudderingly, with something like real regret. 'Among other things, Maggie's snap statements are surprisingly correct.'

'And now you have two to ponder upon!' Carole said in exactly her usual tone, with the same air of serenity that took all sting from her words. 'Maggie could hardly be said to be in the know on this occasion.'

'Wishful thinking, probably!' Katia said before she could stop herself, causing Liz to open her mouth and then stop short with the pained air of having nearly bitten her tongue. 'I think I'll take another dip,' she said in her friendly fashion, and wound up with languorous grace. Susan and Debby, seeing her approach them, challenged her to race. Liz hit the water, calling clearly:

'Moreover, I'll win!'

Carole looked away from the unequal contest. Liz did everything outdoors supremely well. She was really a very nice girl, sincere, uncomplicated, a bit young for her age, in outlook and temperament poles apart from her daughter. Carole looked across to where Katia was lying back in the deck chair, her sun hat tilted defensively over her pure oval face. Carole well knew she had been feeling restive, for her daughter was not a great one for trivia, well sustained. Her reaction, however, came quicker than Carole expected.

'I wonder how many mothers are content to wait like you to receive confidences? You're truly marvellous, Mamma!'

'No argument there!' Carole said with a smile. 'But don't you think you should give poor Ivor his peace of mind back?'

'I'm wondering how on earth I'm supposed to do that? Seriously. I don't love him. That's true, confirming your strong maternal suspicions. I'm very fond of him. He's attractive to me and professionally speaking, I admire him greatly. Who knows, I just could have married him given different circumstances. I do know I shun the thought of hurting him. He claimed once that I used him, and in a way I have. He's been so very kind to me, and he's helped enormously with my career.'

'He denies that himself, dear. He thinks as I do, you're too hard on yourself. Your own ability will get you anywhere you care to go, and you no longer have to fret about me. I'm improving every day, that's plain to see. It's been marvellous for me having you here, but I don't intend to tie you to my side – not my clever Katia. At one time I was hoping Ivor was the answer, but now, of course, I see quite plainly that he's not!'

'I come close to loving him!' Katia supplied, still clinging to an escape route.

'Ah yes, darling. You and Ivor have all the ingredients bar one. What you need, he can't supply, and Ivor can't order up love. It's not an intellectual experiment, a necessity of the head, but the heart and the flesh. It's really a kind of miracle to love at all, and when one's love is returned – well, it's a human condition that will never be surpassed. Those of us who aren't so fortunate settle for what there is available; home, security, children, a continuation of the life pattern of their parents with perhaps more material advantages. That's the normal condition for most people. Even the ones outside the norm like to set up house. Very few of us are so self-reliant we can do without somebody else. Ivor is a man. He has reached, I should say, true adult standing. He must accept an irreversible decision. In a way, I'm sorry. He's a delightful man, but I have someone rare in mind for you.'

'So have I! All hell and damnation!' Katia said so softly, so wryly, her mother laughed. 'I can't see Ivor in Hollywood, can you?' Katia asked, unwilling to pursue the other line.

'No, I can't,' Carole followed cue. 'Not that they haven't a great many writers of quality there, but I keep getting this picture of glorious technicolor, and Ivor suggests a far more muted background. It's all experience for him, all the same. A writer must have these extraordinary adventures, after all. I can't see any reasonable objection to that!'

'Admirable, Mamma!' Katia said, her densely blue eyes veiled with laughter, then she sobered abruptly. 'It's not going to be easy.'

'It never is, but it has to be done, and to delay the telling is downright unkind, not to say unfair!'

'You've made your point, Mamma. I love someone else,' Katia said suddenly with a funny little gasp as though the breath had been struck from her body.

'Yes!'

'Is it that obvious?'

Carole gave her daughter her full, unswerving attention. 'I'm your mother, remember. Little of what you do lately is coincidence, my own little friend. You have a very special place in Thorn's affections, we do know that,' she went on, switching easily to the plural. 'But what else do we know? You must admit he's uncommonly difficult to fathom. In lots of ways he leads a subterranean life. He's not the man to give a thing away unless he feels so inclined. Often he sees you as the child you were. It's apparent in the way he looks or smiles — remembrance of things past. I'm sorry, my darling, but I'm not much help to you there. Much as I love him, I haven't a clue what Thorn's thinking from time to time. Now, Liz — that's a different matter. She's a bubbling brook. She'll sparkle away without intermission for the next few days and for only one reason. Thorn is any woman's idea of romance in the grand manner. Who can blame her?'

'On the contrary, Mamma, I don't. I even like her. I think she'd be good for Thorn!'

'Of all the ridiculous . . .' began Carole.

'Meaning me?'

'Meaning you. My darling child, that's very generous-natured of you, but I would lay a heavy wager Thorn is being driven slightly up the wall. He couldn't get out and about fast enough this morning. You must bear in mind that he's a pretty complex man — thoughts and ideas, his prides and his pleasures. He's by no means a purely physical type, man on the land and all that kind of thing. He has no time at all for childishness, however charming. I wouldn't care to be the woman to satisfy him, if you take my meaning correctly. He's far more the connoisseur than my dear Charles ever was, would that I could have him back. No, my darling,' she continued lightly, 'Liz may be putting up a bold play, but she has no chance with Thorn!'

'She has Maggie's backing!' Katia supplied.

Carole audibly clicked her teeth. 'It doesn't add one hairsbreadth to her chances! You've always seen Maggie as larger than life-size, pet. She has no influence on Thorn and to the best of my knowledge she never has done. Why, it was an open conspiracy between Charles and Thorn to allow her to think that she had. Her nature demands it and it made her happier.'

Katia was prepared for the old argument. She smiled a little ironically, but her voice was quite dispassionate. 'I don't think they knew her in her deepest, darkest depths. Even you don't know her, Mamma. Oddly enough, *I* do!' What had been long in her heart, never uttered, now surfaced. 'Maggie is twisted!'

There was a stricken little silence, then Carole was startled into speech, tiny lines forming about her mouth, the fine planes of her nose. 'Oh, darling, not *that* again! I know, none better, she can be excessively disagreeable, like a whole plague of grasshoppers, but twisted? Rather another frustrated human being.'

At the distressed note in her mother's voice, Katia quickly reversed her attitude, and gave a wide, unconcerned smile. 'All right, sweetie, have it your own way. She's a frustrated dowager duchess, head of the clan. This is her world out here – Miss Maggie McCabe of Carunya!'

'A courtesy title,' Carole said placidly. 'I've never aspired to be a matriarchal figure myself!'

'No, thank God!' Katia answered piously; straight-backed, head tilted back, at the ready like a ship about to sail. 'You're our mother. Debby and Sue and I love you for being just what you are. You're looking so well and pretty we'll be everlastingly grateful to Sarah for looking after you so well – and here she comes now. I think I'll take Jamba out, do you mind?' She stood up and dropped a kiss on her mother's soft curls.

'Not at all, darling. I'd come myself, only these days inclination must give way to common sense. Probably you'll come back knowing your own mind a whole lot better.'

'I hope so, Mamma!' Katia turned around to smile at the approaching Sarah, the blue of her eyes echoing the blue of her hat, the sun on her cheekbones, the lovely matt skin. Sarah who loved beautiful things was enchanted. *And* her manners were beautiful as well. Miss Liz Dickinson, for all her nice ways, made a very clear distinction between staff and family, infusing into her voice with the former a note that stopped just short of arrogance, lest they aspire to equality. It amused Sarah rather than annoyed her, for she had a great sense of humour. Miss Katia was entirely different, in Sarah's book a 'real lady'.

Down at the jump-up, McCabe tossed off his kerchief and strode out of the mêlée of moving cattle. A tall, lean man with wide shoulders, a figure of steel and muscle. His face was hard and intent as he tossed a few words over his shoulder to his foreman, a moving figure on horseback, almost lost in a red fog of dust. Never far from the Boss, hovering in the background, was Left Foot Charlie, the old aboriginal stockman and incomparable master of the bush, so named because of his lifetime devotion to Charles McCabe, shadowing his master's footsteps since they had both been boys in the great Outback. This allegiance had now been transferred to Thorn – not as a matter of course, no aboriginal gave his loyalty haphazardly, but because Thorn McCabe had proved from almost the time he could toddle that he was his father's son, a man that a proud old elder of the Eaglehawk tribe could follow with honour.

Katia threw up her head with intense pleasure. Even at a distance, dressed just like the rest of his men, some of them of a similar, tall rangy build, it was easy to pick Thorn, a man among men in a world unchallenged by women. The Boss Man. The air of authority was apparent, the unique kind of elegance in the way he moved, the flash of white teeth in a dark, sculptured face. There was danger here, among hooves and horns and a solid, jostling wall of powerful flesh. She gave an odd little shudder, remembering . . .

She had been fourteen when she had witnessed her first stampede. They had made an overnight camp after droving a big mob in from the sandhills. She was unlikely ever to forget it; a terrifying spectacle all the more frightening because it had been played out in bright moonlight, ghostly. The tumult, the devastation, the bellowing and pitiless onslaught like a mind-paralysing landslide, the whistle of terror from Jacky Mulowrie, who went down under the thundering black army, all for upsetting a few pots and pans, tripping over a clump of spinifex still with a few cubes of sugar in his hand, lurching desperately out of the path of the bellowing furies. She couldn't bear the thought of it, even now, though Jacky had never screamed, never made another sound. The episode had caused her more than her share of nightmares when she relived those violence-packed moments when Thorn and his father and old Charlie Left Foot had cut diagonally across the face of the stampeding mob, riding close to death from trampling and slashing white horns, swinging the frantic, fear-crazed cattle away from the river and mass suicide.

She had never told her mother and neither had the men, seeing nothing to be gained in upsetting her. Thorn had comforted her then and she had been nearly hysterical, half in and half out of the fork of the paperbark where he had shoved her, covered in twigs and dust and tears. She had been violently ill afterwards and he had held her head, washing her face for her, as much a part of the contretemps as the good times. What they could find of Jacky they buried, with Left Foot Charlie more furious than sorrowful and only Katia to shed a tear, a woman first and last and never a cattleman, iron hard in the burning sun, full of a cool daring and courage in the brilliant, moon-washed, devastated landscape. If they had been angry, silently contemptuous of a foolish boy's prank, she for one couldn't sit in judgment, when all of their lives had been at stake without counting the loss of stock.

Her mouth was a little dry and Katia swallowed, trying to free her mind of her unsummoned recollections. Thorn had seen her and was moving easily towards her, his whole aspect changing. She watched him, he had a way of walking that was all his own — easy fluid movements, noiseless like a cat walking on rice-paper. His head, for a moment free of the pearl-grey Stetson, had the same sheen as the hide of his own magnificent stallion, Rimfire, the lord of the stud.

His skin was a deep copper bronze. Really he was as dark as an Indian. A little helplessly she smiled, her face lighting to radiance. She could sing. She could shout. She could act anything out. Where Thorn was was exultation and a deep content. The shimmering density of her eyes was enough to tell him that. He looked up at her sitting so lightly on the little filly, deceptively fragile when he knew she could handle just about anything in his stable. All except Rimfire – he denied her that; the stallion was too powerful, temperamental too, a one-rider horse.

He greeted her with lazy indulgence, then turned to caress the filly, knowing she couldn't bear to be ignored. Indeed she had formed the habit, now broken in case she damaged herself, of kicking the stable door when she considered herself neglected. He stroked the satiny neck and Jamba nuzzled into the man's shoulder, rather absurdly like a female of another species.

Katia laughed her eyes glowing like sapphires and the man, looking from the filly to the girl, smiled. 'Now that's what I call affection. She's a wayward little thing and she's got a temper too, but I think she's probably the most beautiful creature I've ever seen, outside of you!'

The sun struck a silver flash from her eyes. 'Now that's what I call a friend!'

'You've always needed a friend, Kat. I *am* your friend.'

'Within limits!' she said with a bravura challenge, the long veiling of lashes over the intense blue of her eyes.

'Are you making some kind of accusation?'

'No, only an inquiry!' she murmured in a silver, ironical voice, looking down at him. Duty, compassion, friendship, he had those to offer, but love . . . none. Their glances had met and locked like magnet to steel, but she couldn't free herself of this unshakeable fixation. I love you, she thought, with futile perplexity.

His black brows tilted. 'Are you attempting by any chance, jewel-flower, to seduce me?'

'On the contrary,' she said, her face high-boned and controlled.

'Life is full of small disappointments. And the prospect's rather limited while you're up on that horse. Come on, Kat, show a little mercy, have a cup of coffee, then we'll go for a ride. I've earned a break and you can have the honour of riding beside me!'

'Master, hear me, I've always been your servant!'

'Why not, when I've trained you myself!' One moment she was up on the filly, next she was standing on the ground, swaying lightly, his precise, dark-shaded voice very sardonic in her ear. 'Patience is a virtue, Kat, not mine.'

'Nothing else could account for it!' She stopped, gasping a little as his hand came up under her hair to grasp the back of her neck. Excitement ran like the wind through her nerves. With her cheeks flushed, her eyes sparkling, her cameo face took the breath away.

'No more flower-tipped arrows or I'll have no choice. A pity, when I'm so gallant!'

'Actually I was thinking patience isn't the only virtue you appear to be without!'

He raised his eyebrows at her suddenly wilful face. 'If it's a trap, Kat, it's very delicately baited. I could put one hand around your neck . . .' For an instant the full weight of his arm was in his hand, then he relented, laughing beneath his breath. 'But not now. You make an exquisite enemy, but I told you I'm your friend. All your life you're going to need someone to look out for you.'

'And who would do that?' she demanded.

'I will until you can find someone better. It's easy when you know how!'

Her eyes suddenly filled up with traitorous sparkling tears and Thorn dropped a hard, effective hand on her shoulder. 'It's quite an affliction to be highly strung! Quiet now, Kat, beautiful as a bird. I want you where I can see you. Besides, Casey makes very good coffee!'

Unpredictable as always, he gathered on his finger-tip the single tear that had descended her cheek and touched it to his mouth. 'The faithful are sweet, the wicked sour. Relax, Kat, you can't get rid of some people no matter how hard you try!'

She began to laugh a little helplessly without looking up, thinking it a very accurate assessment of her plight, and he continued with a faint edge, his black slanting eyes sparking fire.

'No empty threat! Now, you get the coffee, you know how I like it, and I'll get some of this dust off.'

With a soft little sigh of obedience, and he never expected anything else whatever the books said, Katia walked off to the fringed shade of acacias with their neat perimeter of grass and the long wooden table set up well clear of the dust arena. Coffee. Hot, strong, no milk and three sugar. She could handle *that*! She was thirsty herself.

'Hello!' she said sociably to the few hands who were standing about, smiling, lifting her face.

They turned as one, looking strangely alike, deeply tanned, same streaks of dust on the face, towering above her, sweeping off their broad-brimmed hats to a man, smiling with good reason at this vision the cooling, fragrant wind had swept in.

'Mornin', Miss Kate!'

CHAPTER EIGHT

Down in the tree-screened gully small brown children, their hair adorned with tiny everlasting daisies, were casting away smartly with supple warrum wands, shattering the water into silver fragments, in the hope of catching some of the golden perch on their way up stream. This was a more remote part of the run, women's country, as ordained by the Dreamtime law, and a favourite gathering place for the women and children of the tribe; full of spirit influence and harmony and conducive to training the children in their kindergarten work. For the moment the lessons were over and a great deal of sport and hilarity was being indulged in.

Katia gave a soft mingled sigh of peace and pleasure, reluctant to speak and break through the web of perfection that seemed to ensnare her and Thorn. Grass birds and reed sparrows fluttered about them as they rode through the massed spent blossom of the pink and cerise bauhinias. The thickets were closing in about them, so of one accord they spurred the horses to the grassy ridge that ran for miles along the lovely long chain of waterholes. It was getting on towards midday and the sun was hot on their backs as they looked about for a convenient place to rein in.

From the distant flats towered red cloud castles, marking a mob, a few thousand living beasts on the move. There was always something doing on a great run – curtain on curtain of red dust, thudding hooves, bawling calves, bellowing mothers, the tumult and the clamour, outriders who were not riders at all but part man, part horse, riding headlong into the milling herds. But that was another world where phantom camels quivered and ran in the silver sea of mirage. Here, the gully ran up and out into a small shallow valley of timbered grassland, emerald green with clover, patterned with white and gold wild flowers no bigger than a fingernail.

There were clumps of ghost gums and some big gidgee, the flowering acacias heavy with the long pods exuding sweet-scented honey. It was soft country with plenty of sweet herbage and wild vegetable-cum-fruit trees, brilliant red quandongs, purplish blue plums, bush tomatoes and cucumbers and pale green shoots that tasted just like spinach. They were not really riding as such; the horses walked sedately of their own accord towards the welcome shade of the trees, unmindful of the tiny painted finches and purple-backed wrens that twittered back and forth with material for their nests, secure in the knowledge that water was close at hand.

In silence Katia slid to the ground, letting Thorn tie the horses to a young limewood. A Princess Alexandra parrot, Noorina Nahlen, suddenly shot into the air, a disturbed glory of pale yellow, blue and green with a pink beak and pink-shadowed eyes. She watched its swift, startled flight. It was an enchanted world, another face of Carunya, and the one she loved best of all. A different world, far removed from the one she had become used to, not realizing that though she had yearned in the past for another life, a view from the top, no city would ever hold her. She was as much a part of this vast, untamed landscape as Thorn was, and he was like the eagles that soared free over the heart of Carunya.

With the lush ripeness of a big red quandong in her hand she lay back on the grass, using her hat as a pillow, her eyes half shut against the diamond chips of sunlight that fell through the trees.

'I'm happy!' she said, biting into the fruit.

'Fancy allowing that suspicion to enter your mind!'

'Why, does it sound silly to you?'

'Never!' He dropped down lightly, noiselessly, to the ground beside her. 'This is the promised land.' Abruptly he took the half-eaten quandong out of her hand and pitched it away. 'Don't eat too much of that. You might finish up with walkabout disease.'

'Would that trouble you?'

'Such a one for asking so many damned questions! Come here, Kat, right where I want you, without the possibility of retreat!'

With a steady, easy strength, as if he had always known how to control her, he pulled her into his arms, subduing the moment when, almost in fright, she recoiled like a spring. 'Be still!' he pushed the hair away from her face, the sound of his voice drowning the outside world. The birds sang loudly in the bauhinia trees, but she never heard them, a wildfire springing up inside her with little hope of control.

'What is it you really seek, Kat?' he asked her in a soft, ironic voice. 'Self-knowledge? If you do, I'll help you find it in just a few moments snatched out of time. You can't alter it, or avoid it, not now . . .'

He held her with every skill he possessed at his

fingertips, looking down at her face, her mouth tender and sensuous, faintly parted as though she waited, a conspirator, a self-confessed follower of his very whim, oblivious of all but his dark face and his brilliant black gaze. The blood whipped through her veins, colouring her skin, betraying her, leaving all her emotions unmasked.

His own face showed no sense of surprise. It was schooled and hard, a mixture of great charm and arrogance. Katia turned her face faintly sideways along his hand, deeply disturbed, trying to fight off a wave of desire so awesome it was more of a torment, but his hand slipped under her chin, the pressure increasing. 'Don't turn away, Kat,' he said in a deceptively quiet voice. 'This experiment, if you like, is definitely worth while. You're a jewel a man could treasure all his life!'

Transfixed, her eyes clinging, her whole being effaced, she turned back to him, wondering briefly if he had always had her in his control. If so, there was little else to do but play into his hands, not realizing that whatever she did would have made no difference at all, for his own will was now too imperious, too driving to be resisted any longer. Thorn lowered his head.

Not even the air came between them. There was no sound, no struggle, only the heat of his skin and his mouth on her own, the crushed scent of the flowering earth. Her mind overturned, her inhibitions shattering like glass. All the yearning of the long lonely years went into her response, reflected in the controlled violence of the way he claimed her mouth, as if it were the cup of life to be drained to the end. Briefly his mouth lifted, exploring her skin, returned to steal her breath away.

The fire and turbulence gave way to a slower, deeper, hunger, that was more terrible again.

All her life she had been waiting for this. All her life she had meant to surrender, her mind sinking beneath mounting sensation, pleasure so intense it entered the portals of pain, moving swiftly with the force of a deluge, carrying her away ... The soft sound she made held in the air and he lifted his head, his hands stilled, enfolding her head.

'Katia my love, you're crying! A drowned jewel!'

The sunlight was pouring down on her, her view altered so that even his dark, familiar face was blurred. 'Surely you must expect it!' she said in a voice little more than a whisper, badly shaken, when his was as softly indulgent as it ever was. 'I've lost my pride a thousand times over!'

In an instant he seemed to retreat from her, yet his hands still cradled her head. 'Is that what it is, then?' he asked, and his voice went very dry. 'Well, Katia?'

She tried to hide from him the sparkling blue torment of her eyes, but he wouldn't let her, his attitude faintly derisive: 'Is it your head or your heart that's set on binding me over?' she said, her mind completely arrested. 'The chosen place. The chosen time!'

Thorn's face closed hard. 'Oh, my God!' he said wearily. 'Failure. I might have known. What you really need, Kat, is crushing, not cherishing. And what of Ivor, wax in your hands? I've a liking and sympathy for the man. Or do you intend to distribute your favours impartially? There are no limits to your gifts, I'm forced to admit. You're superb! I could make love to you for ever!'

With a single movement she fought away from his

grasp, coming upright, the colour flaring across her white skin. 'I see what you mean by gifts! All right, I'll tell you now. At the moment I don't really care. I've decided to marry him – Ivor!'

'You'd sacrifice yourself?' he asked in a voice so light and ironical she could have hit him.

'It's no sacrifice so far as I'm concerned!'

'It's no sense at all!' he said in a voice so hard and final it silenced her. 'You're mine!'

The face that he turned to her was more ruthless than she ever could have imagined.

'What a mind-wrecking honour!' she said in an agitated voice. 'King McCabe! You'll never change!'

'*King McCabe!*' he repeated as though it was the most tedious name in the world. 'You've got that down to a serenade! No, Kat, I won't change,' he said in a hard, taunting voice. 'And I won't let you out of my grasp, for all you're still a rebellious immature child. You'll never come to yourself! Now go home before I'm goaded into doing what I should have done a long time ago – turn you over my knee. Spare the rod and spoil the child. It would only need another word!'

Blazingly blue, her eyes fastened on him, all the turmoil inside her reflected in her wild rose colour.

'You're the last straw!' she cried in a final, furious attempt to defy him. 'Surely you don't think I'm afraid. Me? Why it just might take more time that you can safely spare. You're so damned sure of yourself it nearly chokes me!'

'Now there's an idea!' He got to his feet quite leisurely, hard face, lean body, an inch or so over six feet, lightning-fast reflexes. 'What if I said *I've* had my true fill of your nonsense? It's just possible you'll only learn the hard way. Stay and I'll get the job done!'

'I'd stay if I were a man!' she shouted at him, but into his eyes came such a sparkle of light that she stumbled back swiftly through the sweet, humped grass to where Jamba, a highly interested listener, ears pricked at the clashing sounds, was waiting for her. With shaking, feverish hands she untied the reins and swung into the saddle, consumed with an emotion she swore to herself was rage. The heavy silk of her hair fell across her face and she called to him with bittersweet smoothness: 'I owe no allegiance to any man, least of all *you*!'

The ring of his laugh made her heart leap in her breast. It was genuinely amused and he wasn't troubling to hide it.

'No one could ever call *you* fainthearted! That's a very dramatic statement, Kat, and I cheer every word, laced through with abused innocence and years of resentments and hurt pride and good old-fashioned pigheadedness. But not much good as a weapon. There's no need to draw pictures and give me both sides of your tongue while you're at it – both of them false. It just so happens, Katia Grenville, I know you surprisingly well! Now, go home!' he added deliberately, and she received it for what it was, the white-hot flash of command.

Immediately she turned Jamba's head about, the deepest place in her reacting, unaware. Thorn always meant what he said.

It was such a beautiful evening, they ate out of doors, for which Frances Dickinson seemed very grateful, having been frightened out of her wits the same afternoon, when a six-foot log she went to sit on got up and walked away with a quick spiteful hiss of its forked tongue. The upshot was that Frances was rather subdued, allowing her daughter to shine, and even Liz didn't seem much inclined to do that, especially as Thorn had taken himself off to look in on the newly acquired foal, the latest darling of the stud. The little creature, perfect in every detail, was bred from his best mare, Saratoga, a glorious chestnut, and Rimfire. Everyone had already been down to take a quick admiring peep at the proud mother curled in the straw with her son. Just like a human mother, she couldn't take her eyes off her progeny, or hide her elation. She could hardly wait for the time when she would teach him to run, to race like the wind, to become the most beautiful colt in the whole South-West. It was wonderful to dream.

The meal was gypsy style under the stars and cool lights concealed in the hanging planters: charcoal-grilled carpetbag steaks, hibachi kebabs, Debby's favourites, spit-roasted spiced chicken by way of a change and large roasted potatoes buried and cooked in the coals, served fluffy and split in half with lashings of butter. There were plenty of grilled onions and peppers and tomatoes and the usual salad accompaniments and relishes.

Susan, her long blonde hair tied in a sophisticated knot by Katia, was walking about offering baskets of fragrant, crusty bread, but Debby with her usual neat ponytail came to sit beside her stepsister, her plate heaped with food.

'I'm too happy to eat, aren't you?' she asked Katia, apparently in earnest.

'My darling girl, what would you call *that*?' Katia, who was eating in a very disinterested fashion, looked sideways at the perilously piled plate which would have stopped one of the hands after a hard day's muster.

'I made the cole-slaw myself!' Debby pointed out by way of explanation. 'It was a stroke of genius putting caraway seeds into the dressing, don't you think? It didn't say anything about that in the recipe. I just thought of it myself. I'm like that!'

'Not to speak of the chopped walnuts on top. Everyone seems to be enjoying it, at any rate,' Katia said kindly.

'Isn't the foal gorgeous?' Debby rattled on happily, in an ecstasy of content. 'Tiny little bears and doe eyes and those funny baby noises. His coat's a lot darker than his mother's. I say, wasn't that funny about Mrs. Dickinson?' Debby tactfully dropped her voice to a whisper. 'Fancy her not knowing about Fred Flintstone.'

'The goanna!'

'Yes. Marvellous, isn't he, like some prehistoric monster. I wish I'd been there. Charlie killed himself laughing.'

'It wouldn't have helped if you had as well!'

'No, I suppose not. I don't think she could take a joke. Liz is nice, though, isn't she?'

'Very nice,' agreed Katia.

'Lovely figure too!' Debby speared a grilled mushroom and lifted it to her mouth. 'I think she shows a bit too much of her bosom! Like now!'

'This is a quaint conversation, pet. I suppose if you've got a nice bosom it doesn't hurt to show it.'

'A bit of it, yes!' Debby considered judiciously. 'You

don't show all of yours and neither does Mummy. I can't see the sense of it, after all. I mean, there's more to being sort of lovely and feminine than being physical, lots of flesh and everything. It's more an aura, isn't it, something you can recognize. It doesn't depend on what you wear ... or nearly wear. Some more mustard?'

'No, thanks.'

'You don't mind my talking like this, Katy? I suppose it's very adult.'

'Not at all, darling. I'm here to be talked to. Besides, I know what you mean.'

Debby looked down at her long, daisy-patterned skirt. 'I love this, thank you so much. My first long frock. Sue looks very elegant, doesn't she? My hair will never go like that.'

'Of course it will!' Katia looked at her small stepsister affectionately. 'I could do it now, but you're too young yet, but Mamma said you can go for a swim later when your dinner goes down. If it ever does with that little lot!'

'Oh, good. Liz said she was going in, it's so hot. Are you?'

'Not tonight, darling.'

'A direct hit! I wish you were. You can swim like a fish.' Something happened to the small blonde face – an intake of breath, a funny little grimace, a meticulous look into Katia's lovely, faintly remote face. 'You're not yourself tonight, are you? I can always tell. Mummy said I must have extra-something perception. Are you fretting for Ivor? I do so like him.'

Despite herself Katia laughed. 'Debby, you're perfect – an unspeakable joy! But actually no, darling,

I'm not fretting. I've just got a few things on my mind.'

'Of course!' said Debby idly. 'Secrets. Every woman should have them.' With her free hand and rough small girl gesture she rubbed the back of Katia's neck, causing her to smile. 'When I'm your age I'm going to be fairly bothered out of my senses with them.'

'Well, for now,' said Katia placidly, 'keep my place while I go inside and see about coffee. Mr. Dickinson will be wanting some soon.'

'Busy child!' Debby returned cordially, raising her limpid blue eyes. 'By the time you get back I'll be through all this.'

It was an ill wind that brought Katia back into the house. Minnie was already on her way out to the back terrace with the dinner trolley laden with tea and coffee, an enormous cheesecake decorated with whipped cream rosettes and slivers of chocolate, iced Camembert for Mr. Dickinson coated in fine breadcrumbs and served in a crisp lettuce cup with an assortment of crackers. Katia looked across at Minnie and smilingly indicated her approval, and Minnie looked back admiringly at this wonderful friendly young white woman who actually looked like Helen of Troy, if Miss Debby was to be believed. Minnie had no clear picture of Miss Helen, but Miss Katia was fabulous. Her lustrous black eyes moved shyly over the thick shiny hair swinging back from the brow, as black as her own, the gillyflower blue eyes, that white, so white skin when even the little girls were golden. Minnie rather fancied herself in Miss Katia's outfit, cuffed white trousers and a clingy little navy and white sweater. Only the very slim could wear that, and

Minnie was very slim.

With a complacent little sigh of self-satisfaction and a friendly sweep of her long black eyelashes she wheeled the trolley out into the glorious night. She felt rather dreamy herself.

Katia's thoughts, on the other hand, seemed to be quickening, clarifying, as she was coming to a decision. For the best part of an hour she had been fighting down the compulsion to seek out Thorn, corner that fathomless man so she could deal with the summer lightning that had struck between them. Outside, round the pool, everyone was quite happy. She would not be missed if she slipped away for a while to the observation block, but not in the shoes she had on; glove-soft sandals in navy and white that had cost her the best part of fifty dollars.

She had reached the top of the stairs, moving along the gallery, when a cold, well-bred voice stopped her in her tracks.

'And what would you be doing?'

It was exactly the tone an unpleasant woman would use to humiliate one of the lower servants. It was droll really. Katia swung about in mild astonishment. Even Maggie wasn't allowed to get away with that. 'What the devil do you think I'm doing?' she asked calmly, amused irony in her blue eyes. 'I'm going to my room.'

'With some plan fully in your mind, I suppose?' Maggie asked with some considerable asperity. 'You seem to hanker after punishment, and you'll get as much as you want if you don't take care!'

Katia still looked undisturbed, self-sufficient, with no hint of the anger that was washing over her. 'I've never been able to talk to you, Maggie, and now I'm not even going to try. So far as I'm concerned you're a typical Edwardian spinster, alarmingly forthright. You could even be a little crazy in your own well-bred way.'

Colour engorged Maggie's high-boned face, flushed with a furious pride. 'May I answer that?' she said, moving with astonishing speed for a woman of her build and years, cutting off Katia's escape route. 'If *crazy* is being able to see through your machinations.' She stared at Katia with a swooping relentlessness. 'I must give credit where credit is due, you do persist in the face of every known obstacle. Even with you I never dreamt I'd have to repeat myself, but I see that I do. You're a breed about whom I have no curiosity at all. Leave my nephew alone. He is not for you. When he marries it will last for ever – a sensible, responsible woman of our own kind, not a silly little theatrical dilettante. You've looks, I'll grant you, steamy emotions. Even my nephew is not immune to that kind of excitement, but it doesn't last. Your type only gets passion from a man, not respect and devotion. You're bad for him, bad for Carunya. Need I say more? I'll stop at nothing to protect my family's interests, and rightly so. You see, I was wise to you and your ways from the day you came into his house. It started then, I'll stake my life on it – you and your blue eyes and your tantrums. My nephew defending you at every turn, taking your part against his own aunt. Sister to the father he adored. Oh yes, you got around Charles too, little wild one. Let me tell you, girl, blood is thicker than water. Never be deceived about that. You're out to destroy my nephew, the only creature on this earth I love!' For a moment she looked a little unbalanced, poised on a knife edge, extracting a bitter pleasure from her harsh jibes. Very early in life Maggie had learnt to attack people where they were most sensitive and she knew this girl's weakness, a sharp thorn in her flesh. Katia's face had lost every trace of colour and for that Maggie, the victor, unused to argument, knew a quick sense of triumph. Characteristically, she began to feel safe, but Katia spoke gravely, upsetting the verbal contest.

'You won't believe this, Maggie, but I'm grateful — grateful to you for saying all this. I've known all along that you hated me, but you've never actually put it into words before. There was always that element of doubt, even allowing for the charm of your manner. Always I wondered if part of the blame was mine. Now I see that it wasn't. I had no chance right from the start and I suppose without Thorn between us you'd never have come out into the open at all!'

Maggie threw back her colourless head against the dark panelling. 'Don't speak to me like that. I don't take that kind of thing lightly.'

Unwisely Katia laughed. 'It's a funny thing, Maggie, but the people who never hesitate to fling their unwelcome opinions in others' faces are exactly the ones who are the most confounded when someone carries the war into their own camp! Heavens, Maggie,' Katia's blue gaze didn't look down, 'you look as though you'd like to strike me. You're mad enough!'

'Not yet!' Maggie said with an odd soft voice. 'You're bait for the trap — a creature of little account!'

With a movement, awkward, and totally unexpected, she swept back a powerful arm and brought crashing off its stand a hard paste porcelain lion painted in enamel colours in the Kakiemon style that had guarded the top of the stairs since as long as anyone could remember. It wasn't heavy, neither did it make much of a noise, yet the sound rang in Katia's ears like an explosion.

She looked down at the shattered, beautifully coloured pieces, stunned with disbelief. Maggie herself had inherited that piece. There wasn't a single soul who had ever visited the house who left unaware of that. Katia opened her mouth, but nothing came out. It was inconceivable that Maggie should smash beyond repair a valuable antique and a cherished family heirloom. It was beyond explanation, for the McCabes guarded their possessions to a man. The Japanese lion had always excited a great deal of attention, an irreplaceable part of the house. Every one of them would miss it.

And Katia had missed what Maggie had not – the reflection of a man in the mirrored entrance hall. It was a full moment more before Katia became aware of the soft fall of steps behind her. She knew without turning that it was Thorn. There was no need of the blazing look of confirmation in Maggie's face.

'My own dear father willed that to me,' she said in a dreadfully rigid tone. 'It was, you could say, my great joy, beyond price with its sentimental value!'

Thorn never said a word, nor even looked at what lay shattered on the floor, for all there was an electric aura around him. It was left to Katia to fall to her knees, exclaiming wordlessly, looking very small and frightened indeed – to all appearances guilty, she supposed. She touched the lovely painted pieces with a reverent hand, fitting one against the other with a look of extreme pathos on her face. Wanton destruction, and it must have hurt Maggie, for all she had her reason. She shivered a little as though the cold blade of a sword was about to fall on her neck. Should she wait for it or look her executioner in the face?

Maggie was still talking, wretched, frozen by a dull, resigned kind of anger. . . . 'She's always shown me this dark, destructive side to her. A basic instability, one imagines, like her father. Carole has told me as much!'

It was unholy, shocking Katia into immobility, trembling. A hundred and one childhood misdemeanours played themselves out in her mind, but this wasn't one of them. This was unforgivable, and this time she would say not one word to defend herself. From a great distance she heard Thorn say: 'Leave it, Katia!' and he never called her that, yet it was his hand that lifted her to her feet.

She had seen him all ways – angry, indolent, laughing, vibrantly alive. Now she saw him in a white fury that put glittery lights in his brilliant black eyes. She would willingly face Maggie a thousand times over, but not Thorn. Only it wasn't Thorn at all, but a stranger, an incredibly menacing man. She dared not touch him, or speak to him, or hold out her hand. She was beyond even hearing Maggie's voice, now at last firming into an all-out accusation. Somehow she had always known Maggie would have her revenge. No one had ever really believed her about Maggie, and why should they? First one would have to accept that Maggie was either a fool or a liar, and she was certainly not that. *Up until now!* Tonight's misdeed would leave ripples for ever.

Thorn spoke to her, flung out a restraining hand, but Katia reacted like the Katia of old with all the swift caution and cunning of the wilds. She flew down the stairs with wings on her heels and out into the dark at the front of the house before either of them had even moved. If they would ever move in her direction again. *Maggie.* Her story, she thought, her heart beating so heavy and fast it was unbearable. Maggie would always be believed with the weight of her years and her position and the fact that she had always idolized Thorn, showing to him only single-minded devotion. It was she, Katia, who was the outsider, but a child no longer. If she couldn't command loyalty from the man she loved, she would willingly live in a world of ruins.

Something slithered by her foot, but she didn't care. It could have been a copperhead and it would have been all the same to her. Inside her head a frigid voice was vibrating over and over green with malice like that ring on her finger . . . 'unstable like her father . . . like her father . . . like her father . . . !' Passionately and perfectly she rejected that poison dart. Her mother had never said that. Never. Not to Maggie or to anyone. Of that there was no possible doubt. She knew her mother, in a way Maggie might have experienced with another human being, yet Maggie had the odd knack of making her every word sound convincing, such was her magnificent renown. If she said black was white no one would dare laugh at her or be facetious at her expense. Who willingly courted disaster? Maggie was a McCabe with all that meant, and the whole lot of them had a rare talent for command and manipulation. Indeed, one or two of her contemporaries, to whom she was not altogether unamiable, might even take it as some new manifestation and bow low in obeisance.

Katia winged through the garden, spangled in starlight, like some distraught nymph, chasing her own quick rising temper. The thing Maggie most precisely disliked, like all overbearing people, was an independent spirit in others. It was inevitable that as a child she should have annoyed and displeased her. As a woman in love with Thorn she was an assured antagonist. There could never be the question in Maggie's mind that one such as she could one day become mistress of Carunya, a great station, the beautiful homestead where Maggie had been born and treated like Royalty from that date.

The redwood gazebo loomed up ahead, almost smothered now in yellow gold allamanda, pale trumpets in the starlight. So far as she was concerned, Maggie could plague the entire human race for the next twenty years, but Katia had had enough of her. Let her queen it over the vast South-West, her own wretched sychophants, and when she came to die, probably leaving her thousands on thousands to charity, they would all heave a gigantic sigh of relief. No one, but no one, could honestly mourn Maggie. Even in the grave she would remain mistress of the position.

Breathless from her mad flight, Katia reached the gazebo, her childhood sanctuary, and clung to the latticed door, her slight breast rising and falling. And what of her? What was she doing? Racing like a stricken beast to safety, overcome with shame. It would certainly look like it, but she didn't care. Maggie could continue to tell her edifying story. No, not to everyone, just to Thorn. Thorn was the important one, and Thorn would never allow Carole to be upset. A cold war to the end, just their secret, the three of them. Probably in the morning Maggie, revealing yet again her great strength of character, would refuse to discuss the subject. The lion had been broken, accidentally, what else? and no more could be said. Humbly Katia had to admit that Maggie was pretty imposing. It was a great pity she had lacked certain opportunities, for she could have distinguished herself in many a field. Maggie McCabe was not the common stuff of humanity.

Oh, who cared about Maggie? She was back at the same old game, hiding her heart from herself. There was only Thorn – yesterday, today and tomorrow. Katia ran her hands over the disordered silk of her hair and dropped on to the cushioned bench. Safe as a nightingale in a cage, she thought wryly, outside the reach of anyone who might wish to pull her to pieces. The meticulous arrangements Maggie had made were over. In any case, she was ready to leave.

In a few short months her mother would come to the city to be near the girls, Debby and Susan. They were long since booked into their exclusive establishment which somehow managed to maintain a high academic reputation as well. She would be close to the ones she loved, left with the memory of Thorn to burn brightly, unsurpassed. Let it rest, she thought wearily, her head thumping, but she couldn't even bear to bury what she felt. It was too real in a world ninety per cent make-believe.

The button on the cushion bit into her cheek and she shifted her head fretfully. For the last time! ... the last time. ... Tears sprang into her eyes and she blinked them away like a fierce child. It was about time she developed an ego of her own, but the anticipated pain of loss was too great. A tiny salty trickle ran by her mouth. She lay there, a small, slender girl, with wide, brilliant blue eyes, remembering everything. Her mind could never dart away from the thought of Thorn. There was no peace. He would always be there, to the end. Probably he wouldn't have it any other way. That too, was Thorn. He liked to leave his seal on everything.

After a while the tears dried and she continued to stare into the scented, filtered gloom. She could lie there until morning feeling nothing. *Everything*. Of course she couldn't. On no account at all could her mother be worried. She wasn't an actress, a damned good one – there, she'd said it! – for nothing. She would go back as if not a thing had happened, say good night to her mother and the children, smile at Liz and her parents who no doubt wished her a speedy farewell, all in private, and come back here later on. There would be no sleep that night. She had too many things on her mind.

The stars, like a gauzy sequined veil, were in her eyes. A loosened coil of her hair fell across her face and she swept it away. Never, ever, could she detect his footsteps. She heard nothing, not a leaf crackle, nor a twig snap, nor yet the warning note of a bird – which all came from a boyhood spent in the bush, she supposed. A lifetime of moving as swiftly as silently as a shadow. Charlie Left Foot had taught him that – how to stalk game, humans if need be. The sound of his voice as shimmery soft as black velvet sent fright like a wild thing licking through her veins.

'Where are you, Kat? All right, don't answer. It doesn't matter!'

The impulse to elude him leapt up like a flame. That note in his voice – always so sure of himself. Her head tilted in a new kind of defiance. Fondly he imagined he would find her wherever she was. Well, she too knew a little of bushcraft. Stealthily, very stealthily, she inched backwards over the cushions towards the open doorway, like a small wary cat ruffled up the wrong way almost, but not quite spitting its fury. She wasn't going to be sought out in this military fashion. Before she left she would break every rule, every regulation in the McCabe book.

The hard curve of his arm around her waist turned her heart over. She lifted her hand and began hitting out wildly, not even finding a target. Was Maggie the only one who could make a good fight of it?

'Kat, Kat!' In a way so easy it was insulting, he had her arms pinned behind her back, holding her close to him. 'You're the strangest child!'

'If I screamed you wouldn't like it!' she told him, hard pressed to arch away.

'You *are* screaming in your own way!' he said in a soft, sardonic voice. 'Tearing off without warning like a small wild thing!'

'With good reason, God knows!' she said, throwing up her shiny dark head, the only part of her she could move. '*Let me go!*'

'Not if I can help it,' he responded, suddenly very hard. 'Yell your head off . . . if you can!'

Every grain of common sense, every iota of resistance was drowned from the start. She could despise herself all she liked, but she could never hurdle this enormous handicap. He was implacable to the end, she had one purpose and one purpose only – to capture and retain this moment for ever. She had something of her own to offer. Thorn didn't own all the magic.

If he had thought her superb, wonderfully accomplished, then she was, graced by his hands, his mouth. He could marry whom he liked, but he would never forget her. It didn't seem possible that he was unmoved by this tidal wave of feeling. He laughed gently in his throat, lifting her, walking back into the moon-coloured cage from which she had emerged.

'Jewel-flower!'

The night air was dappled and dancing with light. She lay back on the cushions, pulling his head down to her, lifting her white, slender arms and locking them around his neck, speaking in a fervent, rather dazed little whisper.

'I'll never let you go!'

'No?' His voice was as dark, as sardonic as before and something else again. 'I thought you were going to marry Ivor.'

She tried to frame an answer. What answer did he want? It seemed he had no need for one, could not have listened to her in any event. Lions might have been roaring outside the cage, waiting to get in, but she didn't care. It was worth annihilation to be trapped in a labyrinth of impossibly blossoming emotions, the most wilful challenges that she met and rose to, bewitched and bewitching, set on a brilliant vocation. To give him what he wanted. Warm, silken, her black hair caught in the neck of his shirt, brushing his face. The cool scented darkness was shimmering, breaking all sense of discipline, of time and place. She no longer knew where she was. Only with whom was important – *Thorn*.

She must have cried his name aloud, for he lifted his head, his voice low and clear, meant only for her ears.

'You've found your prison, it seems!'

'I love you!'

'I know.'

Small and white, her blue eyes sparkling, her words came as a soft sigh against his mouth. 'But my mind is my own!'

'I was wondering!'

Always the deep vein of humour, passion alongside, more consummate than ever she could have imagined. 'While I lie here more involved by the minute. Fool that I am ...!'

'May I slip in a word?' he asked, faintly mocking. 'I love you too, spirit child. Human or otherwise. I'm determined to save you come what may, but there's still one thing left to be done.'

'Maggie?' she supplied, trying to search his fathomless eyes. 'She's given you her story, yet you continue to court the strange brat who was left at your door. I don't understand you, McCabe. You must be a throwback to a more tolerant ancestor!'

'Stop that!' he said, faintly exasperated. His lean, strong fingers encircled her throat and he dropped a kiss on her mouth, filled with force and passion. 'Have you no sense at all, or more precisely do you think I've got no sense, that I'd fall for the neatest possible conclusion? Maggie's word against yours and yours of no consequence at all? The McCabes closing ranks? My poor little Kat, what have we done to you?'

'You don't believe her, then?' she asked, helpless under his infinitely exciting touch.

'To tell the truth, Kat,' he said in a rather taut voice, 'I don't give a damn if you'd done it or not! Equally well, I know you didn't. You're not destructive at all, in even the remotest way. It's as foreign to your nature as a seething hostility appears to be common to my aunt's. In any case, I caught the flash of the emerald on Maggie's hand. That, plus the hefty sweep that definitely wasn't yours. I was in the hall long before that, but my poor little lamb, I had to stay put and hear Maggie out — a well deserved punishment, though it was quite invigorating in a way, the dialogue. Authentic at long last. If the lion had to go as part of the action, it was necessary. I'm afraid it's a case of my aunt going travelling.'

'You'd let her go?' she managed to get out, now at the eleventh hour sorry for Maggie, impossible woman.

'My own foolish darling,' he said lightly, 'surely you don't think I'm a keeper of menageries? Tonight's piece of mischief was either inspired by the devil or a freak of misconduct. Whatever it was, it won't happen again. Maggie is more than adequately provided for, even by her standards. Carunya is mine, lest we forget!

168

I don't intend that the light of my life should act as a whipping boy any longer. Besides, I think you'll find Maggie has a great many plans of her own. She has tremendous natural resources, never fully exploited. There are a whole lot of our relatives that need saving from themselves, not to speak of the rest of the world. A good many would be only too pleased to rate a mention in Maggie's will. I understand I'll be struck out of it at her earliest possible convenience.'

'Poor Maggie!' Katia murmured, disbelieving that piece of news.

'Yes, Kat!' he laughed, and touched his mouth to her throat, burying his head in the curve of her shoulder, the satiny young skin. 'That's what I thought you said. Marry me.'

'A request or a command?'

'A command, of course.' The pulse of laughter was back in his voice again.

'Would it matter if it was? Without you there's no meaning to anything!'

'Then your need matches my own. I think I've known from the first your true rôle, for whom you were intended, for all you were a funny, fantastic little thing, full of beauty and grace and a swear word for every occasion. Yet I got used to them. Without me, my lamb, you'll do nothing that's worth doing at all. I always intended to win in the end.'

'So you did!' She reached up a hand and drew him down to her again, and she knew it was a gesture that would be repeated a thousand and one times again. It was right and ordained that they should journey together. Life was no longer a rootless affair, a restless striving after I don't know what, but a passionate desire to live every moment, shared.

Thorn dropped his hand, and her eyes closed, acclaiming his mastery. Whatever she deserved out of life, she had been richly, *richly* overpaid. There was no real kingdom but the kingdom of the heart.

THE OMNIBUS
Has Arrived!

A GREAT NEW IDEA
From HARLEQUIN

OMNIBUS — The **3** in **1** HARLEQUIN
only $1.50 per volume

Here is a great new exciting idea from Harlequin. THREE GREAT ROMANCES — complete and unabridged — BY THE SAME AUTHOR — in one deluxe paperback volume — for the unbelievably low price of only $1.50 per volume.

We have chosen some of the finest works of four world-famous authors . . .

JEAN S. MacLEOD

ISOBEL CHACE

JOYCE DINGWELL

SUSAN BARRIE

. . . and reprinted them in the 3 in 1 Omnibus. Almost 600 pages of pure entertainment for just $1.50 each. A TRULY "JUMBO" READ!

These four Harlequin Omnibus volumes are now available. The following pages list the exciting novels by each author.

Climb aboard the Harlequin Omnibus now! The coupon below is provided for your convenience in ordering.

Jean S. Macleod
Omnibus

An author who has endeared many thousands of readers with her books wherein she frequently uses a background of her birthplace, the west coast of Scotland. The authenticity with which she writes of the breathtaking lochs and mountains, captures and takes the reader with her as the story, in its beauty, unfolds.

.... CONTAINING

THE WOLF OF HEIMRA . . . introduces young Fenella and her love of the Hebridean island of Heimra. Her fiance, Val, the new-found heir to the island laird, and Andrew MacKail, with his bitter resentment of them both. (#990).

SUMMER ISLAND . . . set on the lovely Loch Arden, to where Ailsa MacKay returned when her mother became ill. Perhaps the old romance between Ailsa and Gavin Chisholm might have blossomed again, but there had been too many changes at Loch Arden. (#1314).

SLAVE OF THE WIND . . . takes us with Lesley Gair to Glendhu, where the dark mountain peaks of Wester Ross loomed above the glen. She was mistress of the family estates now, and this stranger, Maxwell Croy was intent on buying back the part which had once belonged to his family! (#1339).

$1.50 per volume

Isobel Chace
Omnibus

A writer of romance is a weaver of dreams. This is true of ISOBEL CHACE, and her many thousands of ardent readers can attest to this. All of her eagerly anticipated works are so carefully spun, blending the mystery and the beauty of love.

. . . . CONTAINING

A HANDFUL OF SILVER . . . set in the exciting city of Rio de Janeiro, with its endless beaches and tall skyscraper hotels, and where a battle of wits is being waged between Madeleine Delahaye, Pilar Fernandez the lovely but jealous fiancee of her childhood friend, and her handsome, treacherous cousin — the strange Luis da Maestro . . . (#1306).

THE SAFFRON SKY . . . takes us to a tiny village skirting the exotic Bangkok, Siam, bathed constantly in glorious sunshine, where at night the sky changes to an enchanting saffron colour. The small nervous Myfanwy Jones realizes her most cherished dream, adventure and romance in a far off land. In Siam, two handsome men are determined to marry her — but, they both have the same mysterious reason . . . (#1250).

THE DAMASK ROSE . . . in Damascus, the original Garden of Eden, we are drenched in the heady atmosphere of exotic perfumes, when Vickie Tremaine flies from London to work for Perfumes of Damascus and meets Adam Templeton, fiancee of the young rebellious Miriam, and alas as the weeks pass, Vickie only becomes more attracted to this your Englishman with the steel-like personality . . . (#1334).

$1.50 per volume

Joyce Dingwell
Omnibus

JOYCE DINGWELL'S lighthearted style of writing and her delightful characters are well loved by a great many readers all over the world. An author with the unusual combination of compassion and vitality which she generously shares with the reader, in all of her books.

. . . . CONTAINING

THE FEEL OF SILK . . . Faith Blake, a young Australian nurse becomes stranded in the Orient and is very kindly offered the position of nursing the young niece of the Marques Jacinto de Velira. But, as Faith and a young doctor become closer together, the Marques begins to take an unusual interest in Faith's private life . . . (#1342).

A TASTE FOR LOVE . . . here we join Gina Lake, at Bancroft Bequest, a remote children's home at Orange Hills, Australia, just as she is nearing the end of what has been a very long "engagement" to Tony Mallory, who seems in no hurry to marry. The new superintendent, Miles Fairland however, feels quite differently as Gina is about to discover . . . (#1229).

WILL YOU SURRENDER . . . at Galdang Academy for boys, "The College By The Sea", perched on the cliff edge of an Australian headland, young Gerry Prosset faces grave disappointment when her father is passed over and young Damien Manning becomes the new Headmaster. Here we learn of her bitter resentment toward this young man — and moreso the woman who comes to visit him . . . (#1179).

$1.50 per volume

Susan Barrie

Omnibus

The charming, unmistakable works of SUSAN BARRIE, one of the top romance authors, have won her a reward of endless readers who take the greatest of pleasure from her inspiring stories, always told with the most enchanting locations.

. . . . CONTAINING

MARRY A STRANGER . . . Doctor Martin Guelder sought only a housekeeper and hostess for his home, Fountains Court, in the village of Herfordshire in the beautiful English countryside. Young Stacey Brent accepts his proposal, but soon finds herself falling deeply in love with him — and she cannot let him know . . . (#1043).

THE MARRIAGE WHEEL . . . at Farthing Hall, a delightful old home nestled in the quiet countryside of Gloucestershire, we meet Frederica Wells, chauffeur to Lady Allerdale. In need of more financial security, Frederica takes a second post, to work for Mr. Humphrey Lestrode, an exacting and shrewd businessman. Almost immediately — she regrets it . . . (#1311).

ROSE IN THE BUD . . . Venice, city of romantic palaces, glimmering lanterns and a thousand waterways. In the midst of all this beauty, Catherine Brown is in search of the truth about the mysterious disappearance of her step-sister. Her only clue is a portrait of the girl, which she finds in the studio of the irresistably attractive Edouard Moroc — could it be that he knows of her whereabouts? . . . (#1168).

$1.50 per volume

Especially for you . . .

A Treasury of
HARLEQUIN ROMANCES
Golden
Harlequin Library

Many of the all time favorite Harlequin Romance Novels have not been available, until now, since the original printing. But now they are yours in an exquisitely bound, rich gold hardcover with royal blue imprint.

THREE COMPLETE UNABRIDGED NOVELS IN EACH VOLUME.

And the cost is so very low you'll be amazed!

Handsome, Hardcover Library Editions at Paperback Prices! ONLY $1.95 each volume

---

Start your collection now. See reverse of this page for brief story outlines.

Golden Harlequin $1.95 per vol.
Each Volume Contains 3 Complete Harlequin Romances

☐ ## Volume 10

FOUR ROADS TO WINDRUSH by Susan Barrie   (No. 687)
Lindsay wasn't sure she could endure this much longer, after all, this "house" where she was now employed, was once her own home. Old Mr. Martingale had been a delight to work for, then the new owner came — a tyrant, a martinet — a brute.

SURGEON FOR TONIGHT by Elizabeth Houghton   (No. 724)
Jan was about to enter a marriage which would salve her conscience, but break her heart. Dr. Ritchie, a man who found little time for play, and even less for women, had the power to spare her this heartbreak, if only he could become "human" enough, and in time . . . .

THE WILD LAND by Isobel Chace   (No. 821)
The little town of Les Saintes de la Mer. The annual gathering of gypsies from all over Europe. When Emma was summoned to France to visit her grandmother, she was not prepared for all this excitement, and even less prepared for Charles Rideau!

☐ ## Volume 11

NURSE OF ALL WORK by Jane Arbor   (No. 690)
When everyone around her seemed to shun her, there was Glen Fraser, the new Welfare Officer. Nurse Nightingale was grateful to him, it would indeed have been so easy to love him, but for the unsuperable barrier which stood between them . . . .

HOUSE OF THE SHINING TIDE by Essie Summers   (No. 724)
Lorette — a perfect nuisance to her stepsister, was finally going to be off Judith's hands, so, to keep Lorette's engagement together, Judith did everything possible. Ironically, it was through the troublesome Lorette that Judith herself found the key to a lasting happiness.

ALL I ASK by Anne Weale   (No. 830)
To heal a broken heart, Francesca decided she must "get away". Wisely, she chose the remote Andorra, in the heart of the Pyrenees. Was it equally as wise however, for her to remain in the orbit of the attractive Nicholas de Vega.

Golden Harlequin $1.95 per vol.
Each Volume Contains 3 Complete Harlequin Romances

☐ Volume 13

DEAR SIR by Mary Burchell (No. 605)
Alexa found herself very attracted to Christopher, and she hoped with all her heart that he would never recall their first meeting. Then, quite suddenly he asked her "Were you ever in Paris?" . . . . so, he had remembered after all.

NURSE AT RYEMINSTER by Ivy Ferrari (No. 874)
Jenny Carr's complete concentration was devoted entirely to catching up with the full year's training which she had lost. When Dr. David Callender appeared on the scene, her attentions became — strangely diverted . . . .

THE BLUE CARIBBEAN by Celine Conway (No. 863)
When Ann Murray, with her brother and sister visited the exquisite Bahaman Island where her husband had left her an estate, the entire white population of Farando Kay was astonished at the three love stories which sprang up from the most unpromising of beginnings!

☐ Volume 18

MOUNTAIN CLINIC by Jean S. MacLeod (No. 638)
Elspeth's cousin Sybil found the peace of mind which she sought, in the lovely village of Grindelwald, in the Swiss Alps. When Elspeth's life touched that of a young Scots doctor, she too found serenity and contentment, the kind which only love brings . . . .

FORBIDDEN ISLAND by Sara Seale (No. 719)
Bewildered and angry, Lisa found herself virtually a prisoner of the dark, remote chieftain of a Highland clan. With each day that passed, on the little mist-encircled isle of Culoran, this gentle captivity became easier to bear.

DEAR FUGITIVE by Elizabeth Hoy (No. 573)
Susan had never considered the possibility that Iain might fall in love, not with her, but with her sister, Jan. In flower bedecked Edinburgh, at Festival time, a time of carefree delight, an "eternal triangle" is quickly taking shape . . . .

Golden Harlequin $1.95 per vol.
Each Volume Contains 3 Complete Harlequin Romances

☐ Volume 16

LOVE HIM OR LEAVE HIM by Mary Burchell (No. 616)
In anger — he fired her, later to find that he desperately needed her help. Anne volunteered, and what began as a generous gesture, developed into a situation full of pitfalls, chiefly in the form of his jealous fiancee!

DOCTOR'S ORDERS by Eleanor Farnes (No. 722)
It was incredible — like a dream. Here she was, in Switzerland, in a world of beauty, luxury and leisure. The events which took place before this lovely fresh Swiss Summer drew to its happy close, were no dream, for Diana, this would last forever . . . .

PORTRAIT OF SUSAN by Rosalind Brett (No. 783)
Managing Willowfield Farm in Rhodesia had made Susan and Paul supremely happy. Then, the owner, David Forrest returned. For her brother's sake, Susan had tolerated his iron-hard selfishness, but how long could her endurance last . . . .

☐ Volume 22

THE SONG AND THE SEA by Isobel Chace (No. 725)
When Charlotte came from New Zealand to Europe to have her voice trained, she did not expect to find her father whom she thought dead, nor to be diving in the Red Sea with him, a charming marine biologist and a beautiful French girl.

CITY OF PALMS by Pamela Kent (No. 791)
On the plane from Paris to Bagdad, Susan had noticed the handsome stranger, with a certain air of aloofness about him. In the emergency which followed, his "aloofness" vanished and he came to her aid, and yet again, in the firghtening wildnerness of the desert . . . .

QUEEN'S NURSE by Jane Arbor (No. 524)
"He has the power to get what he wants", Jess thought bitterly, about this complete stranger. Later, taking up her first "district" as "Queen's Nurse", to her astonishment, she now hoped that this "power" would be directed towards herself!

Golden Harlequin $1.95 per vol.
Each Volume Contains 3 Complete Harlequin Romances

☐ ## Volume 20

DOCTOR SARA COMES HOME by Elizabeth Houghton (#594)
After an unfortunate mishap, Sara Lloyd, a brilliant doctor went to
live for a year in the delightful but remote Welsh Mountains.
Coming to terms with life again, she found Robert Llewellyn
becoming a very dear friend, then, suddenly, out of her "hidden"
past walked — Stephen Grey.

THE TALL PINES by Celine Conway (#736)
Bret was deeply involved in chemical research in Western Canada.
The last thing he needed on his mind was this pale, fragile
English girl, and her foolishly quixotic mission. The "last thing"
soon became the most important part of his whole life . . .

ACROSS THE COUNTER by Mary Burchell (#603)
Katherine was assigned to re-organize one of Kendales' depart-
ments in the Midlands. Within a week, she became engaged to
Paul Kendale while she still loved someone else — it wasn't the
shop, but her own life which underwent the greatest change . . .

☐ ## Volume 21

THE DOCTOR'S DAUGHTERS by Anne Weale (#716)
When the new squire arrived at Dr. Burney's busy and pleasant
household, his presence became a disturbing influence on the
lives of all the doctor's family. It was the eldest daughter, Rachel,
who quickly found that Daniel Elliot was not a man to be ignored.

GATES OF DAWN by Susan Barrie (#792)
Richard Trenchard was accustomed to having his own way, not
least with women. This applied even to his sister, and to her
secretary, Melanie Brooks, who fell victim to Richard's power.
But, in the end, was it Richard, or Melanie, who really did have
their way?

THE GIRL AT SNOWY RIVER by Joyce Dingwell (#808)
Upon arrival in Australia, Prudence found herself the only girl
among 400 men! To most women, this would have been heavenly.
But, what if the most important of these men is determined to get
rid of you — as was precisely the case . . .

Golden Harlequin $1.95 per vol.
Each Volume Contains 3 Complete Harlequin Romances

☐ Volume 23

A CASE IN THE ALPS by Margaret Baumann   (No. 778)
They had always fascinated her, and when the Hilburton family
welcomed Katrina into their close-knit and charmed circle, she
felt closer to them than ever — Then, she realized, that something
was terribly wrong!

THE KEEPERS HOUSE by Jane Fraser   (No. 848)
Amabel was resentful that she had to leave her beloved old home
and live in a small house on the estate. And even more so, when
the new tenant of Kilgenny arrived — a brash young Canadian
farmer — this was unbearable!

COME BLOSSOM-TIME, MY LOVE by Essie Summers   (No. 742)
Jeannie, her young brother and sister, had escaped a cruel
stepfather, and come to the rich farm in New Zealand, where at
last, they were happy. Affection was growing too, between
Jeannie and her farm manager, until the beautiful, unscrupulous
Cecily Chalmers turned up!

☐ Volume 28

CITY OF DREAMS by Elizabeth Hoy   (No. 542)
Three months in a real Venetian palazzo, working for a real Italian
Contessa, and, in the company of Piers Mallory, her most ad-
mired Artist! Julie was so excited, but on arrival, she found things
quite different . . . not at all as she had expected!

DANGEROUS OBSESSION by Jean S. MacLeod   (No. 651)
Faith's fascination for Dr. Maribeau's reputation was so great,
that she married him. His insane jealousy soon spoiled their brief
happiness, and drove them to exile — then, Grantland Orsett
entered Faith's lonely life, only to fan the flame of the Doctor's
jealousy yet again!

UNTIL WE MET by Anne Weale   (No. 855)
The highly successful star of Parisian cabaret was really, Joanna
Allen an ordinary English girl, who longed to settle down and be
loved, in her own home. But how could she convince the man she
cared for that this was really all that mattered?

Golden Harlequin $1.95 per vol.

Each Volume Contains 3 Complete Harlequin Romances

☐ Volume 25

DOCTOR MEMSAHIB by Juliet Shore   (#531)
Mark Travers had little use for a woman plastic surgeon in his hospital in Bengal, but the Rajah had requested her, so he might make use of her visit. An accusing, anonymous letter had preceded Ruth's arrival, and try as he did, Mark could not quite put it out of his head . . .

AND BE THY LOVE by Rose Burghley   (#617)
"Is it necessary to know all there is to know about a man or woman before falling in love with him or her?" When Caroline was asked this question, her answer came easily. It was later that she would have cause to weigh the value of these words . . .

BLACK CHARLES by Esther Wyndham   (#680)
A man who would never marry! Whose character was arrogant and fierce! He was the one dark haired male born of this generation into the Pendleton family, and alas, it was the fate of young Audrey Lawrence to cross swords with — Black Charles Pendleton.

☐ Volume 27

SANDFLOWER by Jane Arbor   (#576)
Both girls were named Elizabeth. Roger Yate thought Liz to be forceful and courageous, and Beth, sweet appealing little Beth. In his opinion of the characters of these two girls, the brilliant young doctor could not have been more wrong!

NURSE TRENT'S CHILDREN by Joyce Dingwell   (#626)
A tragic accident had ended Cathy's training, so she came to Australia as housemother to a number of orphaned children. Dr. Jeremy Malcolm seemed to take an immediate dislike to her organization, and more particularly, to Cathy herself.

INHERIT MY HEART by Mary Burchell   (#782)
The only way left for Mrs. Thurrock and her daughter Naomi to share the inheritance now, was for Naomi to marry Jerome. It might have been a good idea, if only Naomi hadn't infinitely preferred his brother, Martin . . .

Golden Harlequin $1.95 per vol.
Each Volume Contains 3 Complete Harlequin Romances

☐ Volume 30

CHILD FRIDAY by Sara Seale (No. 896)
Friday's child is loving and giving, and this was Emily. But, was she loving enough to be of help to the blind embittered Dane Merritt, and giving enough to share herself with a child who had never known a warm-hearted affection?

HEART SPECIALIST by Susan Barrie (No. 587)
Dr. Daudet was reputed for his knowledge of the human heart. When, after long immunity his own heart was emotionally affected, by a shy young English girl, the famed Parisian specialist found himself learning all over again!

CHILDREN'S NURSE by Kathryn Blair (No. 633)
Linda's ideas on child care were quite different from the Marquez de Filano's, and this young English nurse's quiet obstinacy was a totally new experience for him. So, he began to study this girl — with an unexpected interest . . . .

☐ Volume 19

NURSE ON HOLIDAY by Rosalind Brett (No. 740)
Two gorgeous months of quiet, careless bliss, on the charming Mediterranean Island of Marganeta. Josie was going to enjoy this! Her troublesome brother and her stepmother were disturbing elements, but the real menace to her peace of mind was that dominating, dynamic character, Stuart Mendoza-Cortez Morland.

THE LAST OF THE LOGANS by Alex Stuart (No. 705)
Elizabeth Anson had once refused to marry him. His cousin Fiona bitterly resented his return. Nevertheless, Johnny was on his way from an Australian sheep station, to inherit the Highland home of his ancestors — and things were about to change!

COUNTRY OF THE HEART by Catherine Airlie (No. 789)
Jane had been ill. The post of nurse to a charming small boy on a cruise to the Canary Islands and North Africa was perfect. A series of adventures in the remote heart of Morocco, where east mingles with west ensues — was Jane quite fit to cope with all this excitement?

Golden Harlequin $1.95 per vol.
Each Volume Contains 3 Complete Harlequin Romances

☐ Volume 31

THE HOUSE ON FLAMINGO CAY by Anne Weale (#743)
Angela Gordon was glamorous and ambitious, and confident that in the Bahamas she would find herself a rich husband. The wealthy Stephen Rand was perfect, but alas — he was much more attracted by her sister Sara's quieter charms . . .

THE WEDDING DRESS by Mary Burchell (#813)
Loraine could hardly contain herself, she was going from the seclusion of an English boarding school, straight into the heady atmosphere of Paris, in May. Her only concern was, her unknown guardian — and his plans for her . . .

TOWARDS THE SUN by Rosalind Brett (#693)
There was a warm loveliness all around her on the sun-soaked South Sea island of Bali, yet, Sherlie was miserable. She was exploited by a chilly stepmother and even worse, she fell in love with the totally inaccessible — Paul Stewart.

☐ Volume 32

DOCTOR'S ASSISTANT by Celine Conway (#826)
Laurette decided that Charles Heron was an autocrat, who thought far too much of himself. She also knew that she meant absolutely nothing in his life — a suitable situation? Quite, — until she realized, that for the very first time, she was in love!

TENDER CONQUEST by Joyce Dingwell (#854)
Bridget found her work fascinating. She loved travelling around, meeting and talking to all sorts of people, who all seemed to enjoy talking to her. All, except the new Market Research Manager, who considered her quite inefficient.

WHEN YOU HAVE FOUND ME by Elizabeth Hoy (#526)
During the crossing to Ireland, Cathleen offered to take care of a small kitten. A friendly gesture, which had some far reaching consequences, leading her to some very strange — and exciting results!

Golden Harlequin $1.95 per vol.
Each Volume Contains 3 Complete Harlequin Romances

☐ Volume 34

DEAR ADVERSARY by Kathryn Blair (No. 823)
Grant was an important man in the Copperbelt of Northern Rhodesia, he was used to managing people and things. When he tried to "manage" Morny Blake, she instinctively resisted him, for a woman will be mastered only — when she is loved.

CAMERON OF GARE by Jean S. MacLeod (No. 586)
Fiona Daviot and her father hated the Camerons. A relentless feud existed between the two families. Then, Fiona Daviot fell in love, with the last descendant of the hated race — Iain Cameron, but her father could not forgive!

DOCTOR MAX by Eleanor Farnes (No. 753)
Through Doctor Max Hartland's friendship and her work at the school for maladjusted children, Katrina's grief was subsiding. Then she discovered that Doctor Max Hartland was involved in the accident which killed her fiancee on the eve of their wedding!

☐ Volume 35

NURSE AT CAP FLAMINGO by Violet Winspear (No. 884)
What was really a completely innocent situation, had looked rather compromising. So, to protect Fern's reputation, Ross had insisted on marrying her, but Fern was very much in love with him, and she wanted a better reason than that!

THE HOUSE OF ADRIANO by Nerina Hilliard (No. 840)
Duarte Adriano, Conde de Marindos was not only rich, but charming and handsome. Aileen found that he alternately attracted and annoyed her. The situation results in a colorful story, moving from Australia to Spain . . . .

THE DARK STRANGER by Sara Seale (No. 870)
A gypsy had predicted the coming of a dark stranger, and when Craig Pentreath entered Tina's life, she thought it might come true — but, the gypsy had not said that the coming of this stranger would bring Tina any happiness . . . .